Hypnotism Investigated

Tony Bambridge RGN BSc

New Wine Press

New Wine Press
PO Box 17
Chichester
West Sussex PO20 6YB
England

Unless otherwise stated all Bible quotations are from the
Authorised Version of the Bible, or from Greek and Hebrew
transliterations of the original texts.

NIV – The Holy Bible, New International Version.
Copyright © 1973, 1978, 1984 New International Bible Society.
Published by Hodder & Stoughton.

ISBN: 1 874367 17 5

Typeset by CRB (Drayton) Typesetting Services, Norwich
Printed in England by Clays Ltd, St Ives plc.

Acknowledgements

As Christine and I present this book we wish to thank Christians who stood by us and prayed for us as we worked. We are grateful to our church, Pip'n'Jay of Bristol, who supported us financially and supplied an office for me to work in. The remainder of the financial backing came through gifts from friends and family.

Thank you also to all those who checked over the manuscripts and helped us correct some of the mistakes and imbalances.

Finally my wife and I want to thank our respective families who, at times, came to our aid financially. We also thank members of the family of Jesus Christ who helped us through a difficult time with our young children and our relatively new marriage.

Picture Credits

Contents

Hypnosis and Humanism
Automatic Writing
What Does History Teach Us?

Foreword

by Canon Malcolm Widdecombe
Vicar of St. Philip & St. Jacob Church (Pip'n'Jay),
Bristol

The Bible refers to the devil as one who tells lies and deceives. His aim is to keep people in darkness from the light that comes from Christ. In these present days his activity has intensified. There is a battle on for the human soul. The infernal imagination is very fertile. If one deception fails, the devil has many more to try.

In the realm of theology, he has successfully in many areas legitimized doubt and made faith something to be despised and unacceptable to the intellect.

In the realm of science he has scored a significant victory in causing evolution to be taught as scientific fact, whereas it has little scientific backing at all.

God in his mercy has raised up his people to challenge these lies. He is not dead. He is discovered by faith. He is the Creator. Those once blinded by the theological and scientific lies are being challenged by well qualified men and women in those disciplines to think again.

Thus the devil has turned to another arena where he is having a field day – the arena of medicine. Medicine has limitations, alternatives therefore prove very attractive if they claim to do what medicine cannot. This is not to say

9

that all alternative medicine is the invention of the devil. But we should be on our toes to guard against deception.

I believe that Tony Bambridge is one of those raised up by God to challenge the deceptions behind some of the alternative medicine on offer today. He has written books on Homoeopathy and Acupuncture, and now addresses the subject of Hypnosis. Those in the medical profession must take note of his research and case histories, and Christians both in and outside medicine will deeply appreciate the biblical evidence in chapter five.

I gladly commend this book, and pray its influence will prevent many from deception, and help those deceived to find the truth.

Chapter 1

Introduction

Few people are not moved by the majestic music of Rachmaninov and particularly his best known work – the 2nd piano concerto. Perhaps even fewer people realise that without hypnosis this great work may never have been written, because Rachmaninov was, at one time, so disillusioned with his abilities that he could not enthuse at all about composing.

The story began in March 1897 when Rachmaninov's 1st symphony (in D minor) was performed in Moscow. It was a flop. Many observers say that it was not so much the poor quality of the music, but rather the abysmal performance of it that caused such public disapproval. Some even report that the conductor was drunk. Rachmaninov was so devastated, that nothing flowed from his pen for the next three years. During these three years until 1900 his friends cajoled him and jollied him to compose but to no avail. Friendly chats with great artists such as Tolstoy were similarly fruitless. Eventually some close friends of his put Rachmaninov in touch with a Doctor Nikolai Dahl, a specialist in hypnosis, and after a number of protracted sessions, the depression seemed to lift. The treatment had a rapid effect on his composing and among the many pieces that he composed after this therapy was the enduringly popular 2nd piano concerto.

*This picture illustrates the extent to which hypnosis is being prac-
tised today. From its application in psychiatry, dentistry and midwifery, to its increasing use in music, drama and sport, hypnosis is
becoming something which Christians cannot lightly dismiss.*

In the search for artistic inspiration writers have made
use of hypnosis to create works of enduring popularity.
Lord Tennyson, for instance, used autosuggestion to
release inspiration by putting himself into a trance state.
He would monotonously repeat his own name as if it were
some kind of mantra until his sense of individuality faded
away and he emerged into a level of consciousness which
he felt defied description. Tennyson believed that by sub-
limating his conscious mind in this way he found the
inspiration which he needed.

Hypnosis has more recently become quite popular in another arena, international sport. Competitors in numerous disciplines, particularly rowing, swimming and athletics, are now turning to hypnosis to gain that little bit extra in their bid for medals and fame. It is also common for those in money spinning games, like golf and tennis, to employ their own psychologist, whose job is to raise performance by excluding negative attitudes and energy-sapping pre-match nerves. Since hypnosis and self-hypnosis can be used to allay anxiety and refashion negative thought patterns, it is bound to become more popular among these wealthy sportsmen and women. In other sports like boxing, where pre-bout attitudes are even more crucial, competitors regularly use trance state techniques to relax and prepare themselves psychologically for their fight.

In the field of health and health care, those who practise hypnosis are gaining in popularity as people become more open to novel experiences. Those working in dentistry, in private practice and hospitals, are now using hypnosis for tooth extractions and fillings. Hypnosis and self-hypnosis are also becoming much more acceptable in midwifery where they are claimed to relax the mother and help her cope with the pain of childbirth. Some skin specialists, realising that the available ointments sometimes do not work very well, are now turning to hypnosis as an alternative for patients who have unresponsive problems. The uses of hypnosis in medicine are increasing rapidly, even finding application in the diagnosis of heart disease where trance states are used to recall the occasions of emotional stress that may have triggered cardiac symptoms.

Therefore, with today's hypnotherapists claiming that hypnosis may help with various life problems like stammering, nightmares, accident proneness, weight control and smoking, it is quite clear that the appeal of hypnosis is not something which Christians can discount lightly (see Illustration on page 12).

Is Hypnosis Occult?

Set against these appealing claims about hypnosis is the very real possibility that trance states may expose someone to unwelcome mental and/or spiritual effects. It could be that occult powers are the driving force behind the healing effects of hypnosis.

In primitive civilisations the hypnotic trance was (and still is) very often used as a tool for healing where some form of interaction with the spirit world was essential. The Kalahari bushmen, until recently, used to hold group trance dances to allow a local shaman (or witchdoctor) to exercise his ability to heal those who were ill in the tribe. The women of the tribe would gather round a fire as the sun was setting and begin to chant and clap, while the men of the tribe and the shaman would dance to the beat until they fell into trance. Once in trance the shaman would be able to contact the spirit world, and then begin to touch and heal individual members of the group. Seances similar to this still happen today among tribes throughout the world. In Bali (Indonesia) incense and music combine powerfully to produce trance states in those who participate in healing seances and in nearby Malaysia an educated shaman once explained to a visiting TV camera crew that you cannot see spirits unless you are in trance. He added that a trance state gives a shaman 'his own electric light switch' to the spirit world.

Healing seances, which make use of trance states, are not new to Western culture since spiritualist churches quite often hold meetings like this. What is surprising is that researchers have found that people who have had no experience of spiritualism, often behaved like spiritualist mediums when they were hypnotised. So with the recent use of group hypnosis within ordinary hospitals to help people with diseases that don't respond to conventional treatments, there is a risk that something of a spiritualist nature may occur. Although there may be no deliberate attempt by the doctor in charge to contact the spirit world, these hospital hypnotherapy sessions are still quite similar to the healing seances of the Balinese or the bushmen of the Kalahari desert. If trance states are the way to make contact with the spirit world, is the use of hypnosis by doctors (or laymen) also likely to expose the hypnotised subject to evil spiritual influences?

So is hypnosis inextricably linked with the occult? Do the alluring stories of Tennyson and Rachmaninov simply act as the bait which conceals the steely fishing hook of evil spiritual forces who are trying to trap the unwary? Alternatively is hypnosis just allowing someone to reprogramme your mind for you and, if so, is this an acceptable therapy for a Christian to submit to? Or is hypnosis a harmless phenomenon that can help people discover their true potential?

A Power for Good?

Although a few Christians may regard an investigation into hypnosis as unnecessary, some believers, as we have hinted, may be reluctant to allow someone else to exert control over their mind, and others may feel that trance states expose people to oppressive spiritual forces.

The hypnotherapist would try to alleviate these fears by describing the hypnotic trance as 'daydreaming' or more formally as 'a non-addictive power for good, which is a natural manifestation of the human mind.' They would deny that a hypnotised person loses complete control of his mind but have to concede that trance induction must involve a person relinquishing some control to the hypnotist.

The medical hypnotists, hypnotists who have had some official medical training, are even more adamant that they are in no way dabbling in the occult. 'We are simply utilising,' they explain, 'a natural phenomenon, the use of which does not conflict with any moral or ethical values if handled by a qualified person.' This sounds all right but is it the whole truth? Are these hypnotherapists unaware of the true nature of the hypnotic trance and perhaps misguiding people by what they believe to be simply a natural phenomenon?

To avoid any associations with brainwashing or mind control, some medical hypnotists prefer to abandon the term hypnosis and replace it with phrases like 'directed daydreaming', 'guided imagery' or 'guided fantasy'. The latter is popular among doctors treating children, since fantasy is something which children can readily accept and understand. But whatever the terminology, whatever the disarming persuasive arguments, whatever the well-intentioned reassurances, people still remain suspicious of allowing someone to have unrestricted access to even the deep areas of their personality.

In order to alleviate some of the confusion, this booklet attempts to explain, firstly, what is involved in being hypnotised and how hypnosis is being used to help people with difficulties. Next there is a section illustrating what has happened to some people who have agreed to be hypnotised. Following this there are chapters which focus on the biblical view of hypnosis and on how trance states have been regarded throughout history. Finally there is a chapter on the many trance related therapies that are available today.

Chapter 2

What is Really Involved in Hypnosis?

Since hypnosis and trance states are often misunderstood, it is worth beginning by explaining something of what is really going on when someone agrees to be hypnotised. To make this explanation as unbiased as possible, most of the factual statements made are supported by what has been written by practising hypnotherapists and medically trained hypnotists. If you want to check these statements, all the relevant quotes are provided in the Appendix. I have made every effort to ensure that none of these quotes have been misused or taken out of context.

Trance Induction

Most authorities are agreed that a trance state is 'an altered state of consciousness in which a hypnotist can insert suggestions into the mind of the hypnotised person'. People consent to being hypnotised, but once in deep or medium states of trance they have no power to curb what is being implanted in their subconscious and are therefore in what is called 'a heightened state of suggestibility'.

How do hypnotists bring about such states? Although there are many hidden and little understood elements, it is accepted by most hypnotherapists that the following factors are involved in successful trance induction.

Usually trance induction involves distracting the subject's conscious mind. This can be done by getting the subject to stare at a swinging pendulum but there are many other ways (see Table 1).

1. The subject must be willing and co-operative (see Quote 'A').
2. There must be some distraction of the subject's conscious mind (see Quote 'I' and Table 1).
3. The hypnotist usually has to manipulate the subject's imagination by using the suggestive power of words (see Quote 'G').

Hypnotherapists are mainly agreed that, for some people, this sort of verbal manipulation may amount to deceit, but since the end product is the patient's welfare, the end is thought to justify the means.

For example, the co-operation and willingness of folk who are initially reticent is often won by skilfully convincing a subject that trance states are merely an extension of normal conscious life. Trance states are likened to day dreaming or the times when we become so engrossed in some thought, that we lose our awareness of time and our surroundings. This is, of course, only half the truth since

---

Table 1
Methods Used During Hypnosis to
Distract the Conscious Mind

One may ask, 'Why is it necessary to distract the conscious mind?' Most researchers believe that the power of suggestion is significantly enhanced when it acts on the subconscious rather than the conscious mind. The conscious mind is able to apply logic to what is seen, heard, felt and smelt, and by this means accept or reject something that is suggested. Therefore a person is thought to be more inclined to accept some idea or proposition totally uncritically if the conscious mind is firstly given something else to do. This is why distraction is an important element in hypnosis.

1. Sight:
(a) Staring at a bright light.
(b) Staring into the hypnotist's eyes.
(c) Staring at a picture on the wall.
(d) Staring at a pendulum or metronome.
(e) Flashing or stroboscopic lights.

2. Sound:
(a) Rhythmic beating of a drum.
(b) Regular sounds produced by a synthesizer.

3. Sensation:
(a) Continuous and regular stroking of the skin surface.

4. Other Methods:
(a) Rhythmic breathing.
(b) Powerful aromas (e.g. incense).
(c) Relaxation exercises (e.g. the progressive tensing and relax-
     ing of the muscles of the body, starting from the head down-
     wards).

---

those who are daydreaming do not lose their ability to accept or reject what goes into their minds, as is the case during hypnotic trance (see Quote 'D').

Some element of deception may also be used to reassure

those who question whether or not they will be under someone else's control when in trance. Often instead of frankly admitting that hypnosis is all about relinquishing control of one's mind and subconscious to the hypnotist (see Quote 'A'), the question may be skilfully avoided while the patient is reminded that the hypnotist is merely the instrument that mobilises healing powers within the subject himself.

Another example of deception can sometimes happen in the lead-up to trance induction. Here hypnotists may well employ certain tests aimed at finding out how much the subject will believe what they say, in preference to what normal reason dictates. One test, for example, involves the subject smelling three bottles containing fluids with different odours. Having roughly identified each odour, the subject is given three more bottles which contain only water, but which are labelled differently. If the subject complies by agreeing that he or she can detect the odour on the label then the subject is sufficiently suggestible and ready for trance induction.

The best way of explaining the actual process of trance induction is perhaps to quote directly from a handbook of medical hypnosis. In this example a well-known medical hypnotist explains how he brings about a trance is someone whom he knows to be compliant.

'...the patient is told to sit down comfortably in the armchair with his hands loose on his lap and his eyes closed, and to commence rhythmic breathing. As he breathes he is told that he will feel his eyelids become heavier and his arms begin to feel more relaxed. After a few minutes he is given further suggestions that as regular breathing is continued he will feel himself becoming drowsy and, at the same time, more and more relaxed. He is also told that he will become less and less concerned with things other than the voice of the hypnotherapist which he will hear distinctly. Suggestions of sleepiness and relaxation are continued in a persuasive but rather monotonous voice until it is apparent that the patient is indeed in a drowsy condition and shows evidence of bodily relaxation.'

In this instance, the rhythmic breathing formed the element of distraction required in hypnosis, in the same way that staring at a bright light or a coin provides the conscious distraction which allows a hypnotist to gain access to a subject's subconscious.

Depth of Trance

Medical hypnotists usually classify five states of trance that indicate the depth of the trance. These are:

1. Hypnoidal state
2. Light trance
3. Medium trance } See Quote 'C'
4. Deep trance
5. Somnambulistic state

These stages are purely arbitrary but it may help us to look at what can be expected at the various depths of hypnotic trance.

In the *Light Stages*, (1) and (2), the subject may firstly experience a feeling of drowsiness and a heaviness of eyes and limbs. As the trance induction goes deeper, the subject may experience some inhibition of the swallowing reflex and other muscular changes making them incapable of certain voluntary movements. This lack of control may be rather frightening, so the hypnotist usually attempts to reassure the subject. Sometimes he will try to show the subject that he is in complete control of the situation by doing something called 'arm levitation'. This basically involves the hypnotist causing the subject's arm to raise and lower at his command. If he is successful, he will raise the subject's confidence and possibly increase the chance of attaining deep trance states.

One recent incident of arm levitation that I heard of, involved a dental student. He was learning hypnosis and began to practise on his wife. During one practice session he was successful and achieved arm levitation, but when finishing he was unable to reverse the arm paralysis and had to take his wife to a local centre for hypnosis, to get back the use of her arm.

Research measuring brain wave activity (EEG) has indicated that, during light trance, brain patterns are being given off which most nearly resemble the alpha waves of light sleep (see Illustration on page 23). Although sleep can be induced by suggestion during trance, the EEG brain patterns recorded during most research indicates that hypnosis is not a variation of sleep, but in the deeper stages, is a unique state of relaxation in which subjects are able to open their eyes, hold a conversation with the hypnotist and obey his instructions, while still remaining in a trance.

It is estimated that at least 60% of people are able to enter light stages of trance without difficulty (see research by E.R. Hilgard on hypnotic susceptibility – 1965–). Sometimes called 'alpha states', light trances are nevertheless effective at increasing a person's openness to what a therapist may suggest. These states of increased suggestibility can be induced by a variety of methods which are not directly linked with hypnosis (e.g. massage, aromatherapy and relaxation techniques). Because these therapies are not usually associated with hypnosis, clients are offguard and therefore more vulnerable. It is also possible that the effectiveness of acupuncture hinges on the induction of an 'alpha state' in which needle insertion acts as a powerful suggestive mechanism for healing.

The *Medium Stage*, (3), of hypnosis is characterised by a more marked feeling of drowsiness and more noticeable loss of control of the voluntary muscles. The most striking phenomenon involving voluntary muscles is 'catalepsy'. In this a limb may be made to be perfectly rigid by suggestion and can be held for a long time in a given position without apparent effort or fatigue. In extreme cases a subject's body can be made so rigid that when supports are placed under the neck and heels it remains completely rigid, like a plank of wood (see Illustration on page 24).

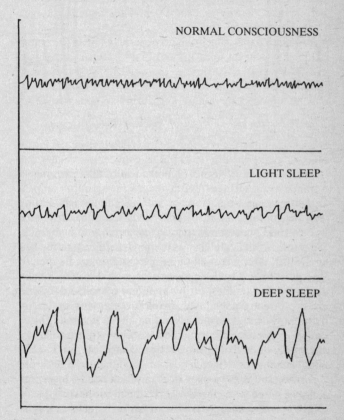

This series of graphs depicts the differing patterns of electrical activity within the brain during various stages of consciousness, as recorded by an electroencephalograph (EEG). The brainwave pattern of a person who is hypnotised shows distinct similarities with the brainwave patterns of light sleep or normal consciousness.

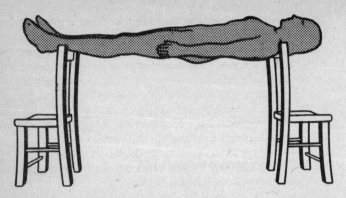

This shows the phenomenon of hypnotic catalepsy, sometimes referred to as the 'human plank' syndrome.

In this stage of trance a person may also experience some sensory changes which means that painful surgical operations can be performed without the subject feeling any discomfort. At first glance it is tempting to regard trance state phenomena such as insensitivity to pain, muscle paralysis and catalepsy as demonic manifestations. But it is worth noting that all these phenomena can happen to people who are under pressure or who are emotionally damaged. Sometimes, for no apparent reason, a damaged or depressed person may develop symptoms of bodily paralysis just as if his spinal cord had been severed. This is called 'conversion hysteria' and has been known to affect the whole body from the neck downwards, or just a single limb like an arm or a leg.

During the various wars of the 20th century some combatants, often with previously distinguished records, suddenly became incapacitated with partial or total paralysis but without a cause. Others were found wandering aimlessly behind the lines in a 'fugue' or trance like state. General Patten and other hard-hearted military leaders may have scoffed at the plight of these soldiers. But common sense suggests that God has created some people with an emotional fuse that, when blown, will cause them to become detached from circumstances that are unbearable. Therefore some trance state phenomena like paralysis, catalepsy and anaesthesia may not necessarily be caused by demonic interference, but may instead be the result of the hypnotist inappropriately tampering with the body's normal defense mechanisms.

It is in the medium stage of trance that the post-hypnotic suggestion becomes effective. This is where a hypnotist implants a suggestion which causes a patient to do something after the hypnotic trance is over, and he or she has returned to normal consciousness.

It is said that about 50% of people are able to enter this stage with ease.

The *Deep Stages*, (4) and (5), are sometimes referred to as somnambulistic states. This term was first coined by the Count de Puysegur who was a disciple of the man responsible for resurrecting the use of trance states in treating illness, Franz Mesmer. The Count used a ritual of 'passes' (intense staring at a subject using the fingers to indicate transference of psychic energy to the subject) to hypnotise his subjects (see photo on page 27). Once he 'magnetised' or hypnotised a young shepherd boy and found that he passed into a deep trance which he called 'magnetic somnambulism'. In this state de Puysegur related what are now regarded as the classic signs of somnambulism, that of an altered state of consciousness in which the subject is perfectly lucid and completely suggestible (i.e. he can be told to do anything within the bounds of his usual moral standards) and afterwards he will have no memory of what went on during the trance.

In these deep states of trance it is claimed that a subject can experience the therapeutic recall of blurred memories and regression to childhood (see later). But other things can happen during deep trance states including sensory hallucinations, clairvoyance (or second sight) and other psychic phenomena, and these events suggest that interactions of a spiritualist nature may be going on.

Other Factors in Trance Induction

1. Passivity

Why are some people more easily hypnotised than others? As well as the obvious reasons already considered other factors may be involved.

From a hypnotist's point of view the ideal subject is a willing one. But a good candidate for hypnosis is not necessarily someone who is naively cooperative. Instead, hypnotists like a subject to understand what they are saying, which can sometimes be something irrational or unusual, but then willingly subjugate his or her judgement in favour of believing what they are suggesting. This sort of co-operation is referred to as 'suggestibility' or 'passivity'. The hypnotist may suggest that a bottle containing water is giving off the aroma of roses, or he may ask his subjects to stand up, and then suggest that they are going to fall over. Cooperation involves imagining the whiff of roses wafting from the bottle or believing that normal balance has temporarily gone and that one is about to topple over. Naturally if the hypnotist gives the impression of being utterly convinced about the deception, then suggestibility is more easily induced.

Children, although not fully convinced of their own ability to reason, can very often discern when the hypnotist is talking nonsense as, for instance, when it is suggested that one particular limb will feel cold although there has been no change in the room temperature. But young minds find it easier to believe what a responsible adult tells them even though it may not make very good sense. So children make good candidates for hypnosis, more especially since they have vivid imaginations that are easily manipulated.

Apart from the obvious deception, passivity or the willing abdication of the gateway of personal judgement in favour of some other person is, I believe, something that God disapproves of. Adolf Hitler was stunningly successful when it came to making his audiences suggestible. With

Suggestibility Testing
In order to find out whether a subject is ready for hypnosis some therapists carry out suggestibility testing. In this test the hypnotist (pictured front right) has asked the subject to stand up in front of him facing away. Having reassured him that he will not hurt himself he then tells him that he is going to lose his balance and fall backwards. If the subject complies by falling back into his arms he is ready for trance induction.

amazing ease he could convince vast assemblies of the absolute necessity of his policies even though most independent observers were shocked at what he was proposing. Perhaps demonic powers were aiding and abetting him, but his fearfully convincing manner was awe-inspiring.

Although hypnotherapists may begin by asking their subjects to believe some mild deception, their eventual aim

27

Is hypnosis allowing someone free access to our minds?

is to create a highly suggestible trance state so that they can insert their own thoughts directly into the hypnotised person's subconscious. It is not the same as having a general anaesthetic, as happens in surgery, because the surgeon only tampers with your body and not your personality while you are asleep. In deep trance, hypnotists are anticipating free access to the subconscious. They are asking their client to open wide the gate of his or her personality so that they can enter and do what seems appropriate to change the way he or she responds subconsciously.

Hypnotists or hypnotherapists will usually protest that they only have the subject's welfare in mind, but their intrusion into a client's subconscious can go beyond the limits that even God sets for himself in his desire to reach out and touch people for good. Jesus says to us as he said to the Laodicean church in Revelation chapter 3, '*Look, I stand at the door and knock. If anyone hears my voice and opens the door, I will come into his house and eat with him and he will eat with me.'* So the Holy Spirit waits to be invited in to the arena of our personalities and, when ushered in, he expects a two-way interaction with us. On the other hand hypnotists attempt to gain access to the house of personality by using subtle techniques of mental manipulation and their client's passive cooperation. Also having entered (i.e. when their client is hypnotised), it is not possible to have a two-way conversation, but rather the subject waits for the hypnotist to suggest what to do next (See Quote 'K').

Furthermore, in their attempt to enter the realms of someone's personality, hypnotists sometimes unknowingly leave their clients exposed and open to the influence of spiritual forces which may then gain a toehold (or worse) and cause more oppression. This explains why hypnotised people are prone to paranormal experiences like mystical visions, levitation, clairvoyance and other extra-sensory perceptions. Therefore a potential client for hypnosis must be willing to accept any trance state experience even if it appears to have an occult flavour. Should someone not be amenable to this kind of paranormal experience, it has been found that deep trance states are harder to induce. Today there seems to be a greater openness to occult experiences, and sadly it will probably yield a harvest of damage in human lives in the years to come.

2. Personality Powers

It is well documented that some people succumb to hypnotic trance induction with ease while others remain rather impervious. In a similar way some hypnotists have a quality of personality that enables them to induce trance states in their subjects more quickly than others. Obviously there are elements of confidence and experience that increase a hypnotist's authority of speech and manner, but there seems to be another factor involved which, for want of a better word, could be described as 'psychic'.

A contemporary example of this kind of personality power can be found in the work of Joe Keeton, a well-known lay hypnotherapist specialising in 'past life' therapy. In order to project his clients mentally back into lives which they claim to have lived hundreds of years ago, he is reported to be able to induce deep trance states in some of his subjects with only a few quiet words.

Charles Dickens, the Victorian novelist (see Illustration on page 31) and self styled hypnotherapist, could captivate his audiences as he read excerpts from his books. J.B. Priestley, one of Dickens' biographers, wrote:

> 'All accounts agree that in humour, pathos or sheer terror, he was unmatched, appearing to almost hypnotise his huge audiences.'

Sadly Dickens allowed this grip over his audiences to get the better of him and in a frenzied round of performances he ran himself into the ground and died prematurely at the age of 58.

Like Dickens or Joe Keeton some hypnotherapists seem to have that imposing persuasive tone, an unusually beguiling manner, and perhaps even some indescribable and strange powers. Although some of these hidden powers may be openly attributed to the occult because the hypnotherapist is a practising spiritualist, many of these abilities probably originate from the therapist's own personality, and may be psychic. This is probably why some hypnotists can succeed in trance induction where a more medically qualified one will fail. This also may partly explain why animals can be hypnotised even though they are neither suggestible to words nor, as in the case of snake charming, can they actually hear the charmer's music (see Illustration on page 32). The overall effect of lulling these sometimes aggressive and volatile reptiles is probably the net result of the rhythmical swaying motion of the charmer's musical instrument, possibly the sound vibrations coming up from the ground and maybe some influence emanating from the charmer himself.

In the case of snake charming, firewalking and other

Charles Dickens is pictured here giving one of his public readings. Such was the popularity of these readings that he could pull in enormous audiences and then almost mesmerise them with his dramatic presentations and powerful personality. Dickens was also a self-styled hypnotherapist and like some of those who practise today, his strong personality may have made it easier for him to induce trance states in people.

This shows the practice of snake charming which is often regarded as an example of animal hypnosis. Though some snake-charmers are probably charlatans, using trickery to overcome the danger of the act, some also can genuinely control these highly dangerous reptiles. The snake, usually a Cobra, is unable to hear the actual music being played, but is influenced by the swaying of the charmer's musical instrument and possibly the sound vibrations that are set up in the basket.

trance related activities it is difficult to say how much is tied up with the individual's personality (psychic), and how much is an occult manifestation. Matters are made worse when respected world authorities boldly state that certain phenomena are the result of subconscious activity when, in fact, they are probably a subtly disguised form of divination. For instance, a well-known textbook on stress and relaxation encourages readers to hypnotise themselves and then study the emanations of their subconscious by using a pendulum. The authors state that the responses of the pendulum to the questions asked are merely the involuntary effect of the subconscious personality on the muscle of the arm that is suspending the pendulum. Even though such explanations have little or no supporting evidence, health experts accept them without question. From my Christian standpoint, asking a pendulum serious questions about one's personal life is a fairly reliable way of exposing oneself to spiritual forces whose designs and plans for human beings are thoroughly evil in intent. In short, pendulum swinging, like Tarot card consultations or I-Ching coin throwing, is no more or less than divination.

Loss of Control

Many people who are interested in being hypnotised very often ask whether or not they will lose some control of themselves or their minds while they are in trance. Except where people are in light trance, the answer to this question is usually 'yes'.

While many hypnotherapists try to evade this sort of question, most have to agree that hypnosis is all about bypassing a person's normal powers of discernment and decision making. E.R. Hilgard, a foremost authority on hypnosis, states that a hypnotist 'uses a number of methods to lead a person to relinquish some control to the hypnotist and accept some reality distortion.'

What kind of loss of control is experienced during hypnosis?

To a certain extent the amount of loss of control experienced during trance depends on how far someone is prepared to go. When a subject tenaciously resists losing any amount of control of their mental and bodily faculties he or she will probably never reach anything more than light trance and will be regarded by the hypnotist as uncooperative.

Those people who do give a hypnotist the necessary

cooperation required for medium or deep states of hypnotic trance must expect to lose some control of their bodily functions. Firstly the hypnotist may be able to manipulate the activity of muscles, not only in the limbs, but also in the eyes, mouth, face, neck and abdomen. Obviously the 'human plank' syndrome, referred to earlier, is an example of this.

Secondly the hypnotist may also be able to produce sensory changes. Feelings of warmth and cold, heaviness and lightness, as well as loss of sensation and the inability to feel pain may all be induced. This last phenomenon has obvious uses, in that minor surgical operations, like the removal of teeth or the sewing up of superficial wounds, can be performed without any conventional anaesthesia. In fact major operations including limb amputations, tumour removal, thyroidectomy and Caesarian section have all been carried out using hypnosis as the only method of pain control.

Thirdly, those who consent to deep (and perhaps medium) trance states will inevitably lose control of their mental and emotional faculties while they are hypnotised. The hypnotist will then be able to insert into their minds ideas and suggestions concerning changes in their behaviour and thinking which they will not remember about when the trance is over. After a great deal of research, Hilgard and Hilgard have concluded in their report of 1975 that subjects will not experience a suggestion as real or act upon a suggestion that would be offensive to them in waking life. Although there are exceptions, hypnotised subjects do not feel that they must do what the hypnotist suggests but they see no reason why they should not comply. As we shall see when we examine the criminal use of hypnosis, the exceptions usually happen when a hypnotist firstly reprogrammes the subject's moral values by altering or distorting his or her view of right and wrong.

Most hypnotists would deny that they are brainwashing their clients, but this is only because they do not employ coercion or violence to break down any conscious resistance. I believe that hypnotism and brainwashing do have

34

similarities, and the only significant difference is that hypnotherapists use persuasive arguments, not coercion, to gain their client's cooperation to reprogramme the way in which he or she thinks and acts. Brainwashing also implies some element of evil intent, whereas hypnotherapists would justifiably protest that they are only reprogramming the client's mind for his or her benefit.

Hypnosis and Crime

Perhaps the most criminal use of a type of hypnosis during the 20th century was the brainwashing of a large part of the population of Germany by Adolf Hitler. In the 1930s Hitler addressed many thousands of Germans at highly organised rallies, and by using the dynamics of mass hypnosis he made the outrageous crime of the annihilation of the Jewish people seem acceptable, even necessary. Assisted by demonic power, he manipulated a vast nation and persuaded them to support him in his plans to conquer the world, and create a new era that would last for a thousand years.

Less dramatic is the use of hypnosis by individuals who have criminal intentions. George du Maurier based his famous book *Trilby* on his experiences at the Gleyre's school of art in Paris during the 1850s. In it he created an egotistically powerful character called Svengali, who found that he could, by his hypnotic powers, transform a shy and retiring laundry girl called Trilby into a highly successful and financially lucrative music hall singer. Despite attempts to rid herself of Svengali's influence Trilby is drawn back and projected into stardom by his overwhelming power. In a nailbiting finish, a battle between the forces of good and evil ensues until Svengali's grip over the girl is finally broken when he collapses dead from a stroke during one of her performances. Set free from his power Trilby is suddenly bereft of her singing ability and rushes off the stage into the arms of those who really care for her. Since this book was based on real events and characters in du Maurier's life it poses the question, 'can individuals really be made, by hypnosis, to do something against their own will, things which perhaps are antisocial or even criminal?'

Most researchers into the criminal use of hypnosis would answer 'yes' and then attempt to explain the necessary circumstances. For instance Jack Watkins, a renowned American researcher into hypnosis, states in his book that 'hypnotic suggestion, when used indirectly and subtly, can cause some subjects to perform antisocial and criminal acts which they would not normally do.' André Weitzenhoffer, another eminent authority on hypnosis, agrees with this statement but qualifies it by saying that this can only happen 'if the subject is made to perceive his actions as not being antisocial'.

A well publicised incident dating back to 1934 illustrates this, and highlights that very suggestible people can not only be forced into trance against their own will, but also be made to do things that they would not normally do.

Case History HYP/A

In 1934 a woman was travelling in a train and fell into conversation with a man who called himself a healer. When they arrived at their destination she agreed to have coffee with him but when he took her hand to show her the way she suddenly felt dizzy, weak and insecure. She felt as though all her will had been drained from her. He took her to a hotel and having placed her in a trance, raped her and made her prostitute herself and give him the proceeds. This dreadful crime only came to light when the police got involved because the woman made several attempts to kill her husband on the instructions of the hypnotist. The police psychiatrist found a way of getting round what the hypnotist had suggested to the woman and succeeded in convicting the man.

This next case history is more up to date and is more directly concerned with the use of hypnosis for therapeutic purposes. Although hypnotherapists have quite strict codes of conduct laid down for them to abide by, sometimes things go wrong. Incidents such as these are probably uncommon but they illustrate the vulnerability of the hypnotised patient.

Case History HYP/B

In 1986 Alison (not her real name), a woman living in the London area who had a rather scarred childhood, was beginning to realise that she really needed help. Becoming a little disillusioned with the counselling facilities available to her in her local hospital, Alison began to enquire about hypnosis. She saw one hospital based hypnotherapist who did not help that much and so she began to look elsewhere. Eventually, through an advert in a local newspaper, she began to attend group hypnotherapy sessions which were run by a private hypnotherapist.

The sessions were informative but did not help Alison to overcome her emotional difficulties. The hypnotherapist saw this, and offered to give her and another girl with similar difficulties, individual hypnotherapy. Although Alison was keen to take up the offer she had to confess that she had no money to pay for the treatment. The therapist decided to waive his fee but reminded her that she would have to see him every week for a fairly long time if she was to get better.

Alison began these weekly visits to the hypnotherapist who managed to induce her into quite deep states of trance. After the sessions she could remember nothing very clearly but she now seems to recall how the hypnotist suggested during trance that her body would be temporarily anaesthetised. Despite this Alison often left these sessions feeling that she had somehow been tampered with.

At the end of her last visit, her trance state was terminated too early and Alison woke up to find her dress undone and the hypnotherapist pulling on his socks. With her suspicions already roused, this discovery gave her the resolve never to go back. Alison told me, and I believe quite reliably, that this hypnotherapist was probably taking advantage of other damaged and emotionally vulnerable women.

Aside from the sexual abuse it seems that the hypnotherapy also caused some physical problems (which perhaps have spiritual roots). For Alison has found that, since her experience of hypnotherapy, she has been plagued with bronchitis, asthma and hayfever. Also under some circumstances she is easily tipped back into a trance state.

Furthermore her painful encounter with hypnosis compounded Alison's emotional problems, and she has since had to wrestle with an addiction to illegal mood-altering drugs. Although Alison has begun to trust Jesus personally and will never go back for any form of hypnotherapy, I am compelled to pray that the Body of Christ will continue to look to the Holy Spirit for the necessary ministries, so that we will be able to meet the real needs of Alison and those with similar difficulties.

Occult Influence

Aside of the obvious risk of being abused while in trance, perhaps the most off-putting aspect of hypnosis for those considering its use is its connections with the occult. Although the induction of a trance by a medically trained person for reasons of health care may seem utterly divorced from any occult influence, both the Bible and the history of hypnosis imply that some form of spiritual interaction is possible when someone enters a trance state.

Spiritualist mediums, tribal shamans and witchdoctors, Hindu or Buddhist gurus, and those overtly involved in witchcraft all consider that trance states are essential for any serious interaction of a spiritual nature. As we have mentioned in the introduction, one Malaysian shaman said that a trance state was like an electric light switch to the spirit world. So as well as exposing the subconscious of a person to the suggestions of the hypnotist, trance states may well also lay open the human personality to some form of interaction with spiritual powers. What depth of trance is necessary to promote this kind of spiritual experience is not clear, but it is not unreasonable to conclude that the deeper the trance state, the more likely it is that a person will be exposed to occult forces.

Most protagonists of hypnotherapy in the western world will strongly deny that their trance induction involves the occult. However, it is unlikely that anyone can be absolutely sure that a deeply hypnotised person is not being affected by occult powers, especially when research indicates that experiences of a mystical nature are not uncommon even in a totally clinical environment (see Appendix Quote 'E' and 'M'). Perhaps if humans at any time allow their conscious minds to be distracted to the degree that a man or woman can suggest and implant ideas of which they have no knowledge, memory or veto, then it is also possible that they are vulnerable to other extraneous agencies which may not have such similarly benign motives.

Termination of Trance States

In the late 1940s, stage show hypnosis became very popular. People, who considered themselves impervious to the hypnotist's power, found themselves whinnying like horses, eating onions as if they were apples and hugging brooms because the hypnotist suggested that they were their girlfriends. Perhaps these shows were great fun to watch, but for some members of the audience there were problems, as they were hypnotised without being aware of it. So when the show was all over and everyone was going home, suddenly friends and relatives discovered they were in a form of trance. In a desperate search for help they were taken back to the auditorium, sometimes only to find that the hypnotist had already left and was on a plane bound for the other side of the world!

Occasionally those who participated on stage continued to hallucinate according to the hypnotist's instructions long after the show had finished. They were told that the hallucinations would have gone when the trance state was terminated or when they woke up from a normal sleep, but this was sometimes not the case. One Christian man who had participated in stage show hypnosis complained to me that long after the event he would fall asleep if someone snapped their fingers in front of his eyes. This worrying problem was only resolved when he was prayed for by some fellow believers.

Although the 1952 Hypnotism Act banned the use of hypnosis for entertainment in Britain, today, in the interest of health, welfare and research (and sometimes illegally for fun), people still willingly allow themselves to be hypnotised. But hypnotherapists have learned from these farcical but extremely serious stage show casualties and have constructed ethical guidelines, for all registered hypnotists, that insist on a thorough termination of all trance states.

Medical hypnotists would say that their professional guidelines are even more stringent and that there are no risks or after effects due to the improper termination of trance states.

Therefore before a subject is woken from trance, all unwanted suggestions, like those about changes of sensation and muscular paralysis, are reversed as are any suggestions about tiredness or drowsiness. Instead suggestions are inserted which imply alertness, fitness, well being and normal consciousness. Once a hypnotist is satisfied that all unnecessary suggestions have been removed, then the subject will be woken slowly from trance. Sometimes this involves instructing the subject that his trance will terminate when the hypnotist has completed a count of one to ten.

Trance termination, especially of deep trances, does not always run a predictable course. Occasionally the hypnotist will not be able to reverse something suggested during trance and will need to seek the help of a more experienced hypnotist. In some cases, where subjects induce their own trance state (self-hypnosis), things can go badly wrong if they are not instructed about how to choose carefully their trance induction and termination signals. Having said this, most hypnotherapists believe that when a patient cannot be woken from trance, they should be left alone to sleep it off and they will wake up normally.

When the subject has woken up, it is quite usual for them not to remember what has transpired during the trance. In fact trance state amnesia is one of the signs that a person has been quite deeply hypnotised. Sometimes those who have been only lightly hypnotised will remember some of what went on during trance, but often a subject will neither recall trance state experiences, nor be able to distinguish between his own subconscious thoughts and those that were placed there by the hypnotist. Oddly enough this kind of amnesia often makes people believe that they were never really hypnotised. But, on further questioning, it is evident that they must have entered a trance state because they cannot remember any of the mandatory suggestions that formed the basis of their treatment.

Chapter 3

Hypnotherapy Today

People who are drawn to hypnosis as a form of treatment often have health difficulties which the conventional medical profession is unable to deal with. These difficulties may include unbreakable negative habits (e.g. smoking), areas of difficulty within sexual relations, skin disorders, insomnia, psychosomatic disorders and emotional problems. Even some surgical procedures are performed with the anaesthesia (loss of feeling) that can be induced by trance states (for a detailed list of the therapeutic uses of hypnosis, see Table 2).

The main aim of the hypnotherapist is to induce a trance state deep enough for the appropriate treatment and as I have already mentioned most treatments involve the induction of at least a medium depth of hypnotic trance. Since the subject may well not reach this depth of trance at the first attempt, the hypnotist will have to employ trance deepening techniques to help the subject achieve the appropriate level of trance.

Trance Deepening

Most trance deepening procedures usually involve the hypnotist making further suggestions about increasing drowsiness and relaxation. One way in which this can be done is to get a hypnotised subject to imagine that he is in a lift that is going downwards. He is told that as the lift

Table 2
The Therapeutic Uses of Hypnosis

1. In Medicine:
Treatment of
(a) Asthma
(b) Migraine
(c) Blood circulation problems
(d) Raised blood pressure
(e) Diabetes
(f) Bed wetting
(g) Warts
(h) Skin problems (e.g. eczema)
(i) Cancer – usually only attitude improvement
Hypnosis is also used in pain control and has been used as an aid in the diagnosis of heart problems.

2. In Surgery:
(a) Reduction of anxiety in the pre-operative stage
(b) Pain relief during surgery
(c) Post-operative pain relief

3. In Obstetrics:
(a) In decreasing the duration of labour
(b) In reducing the need for painkillers

4. In Dentistry:
(a) In reducing anxiety
(b) Pain control during tooth extraction etc.
(c) Post-operative pain relief

5. Other Uses:
(a) Sex therapy
(b) Weight control
(c) Stress management
(d) Help with habit breaking (e.g. smoking)

descends from floor to floor his level of trance will deepen. When a sufficient depth of trance has been reached the subject is instructed to imagine that he will leave the lift at the next floor. When the lift doors finally open the hypnotist will begin to paint an imaginary fantasy that best suits the subject's needs.

Another method of trance deepening is the repetitive use of trance induction and termination. This last technique is sometimes called the 'fractional method' and consists of hypnotising the subject as deep as possible and then, just prior to waking, implanting the suggestion that he will be able to gain deeper states during subsequent trances. Almost immediately (or during another session) the subject is re-hypnotised, hopefully to a deeper state. Whatever technique is employed, quite a number of prolonged sessions may be required before any specific treatment can be started. Some believe that the greatest depth of trance is attained during the period between the fourth and the twelfth session.

When a sufficient depth of trance has been achieved, the hypnotist has the choice of two main hypnotherapeutic techniques. The first is the use of prohibitory suggestion, where the hypnotist suggests to the hypnotised subject that any symptoms of pain or emotional problems no longer exist. In the next chapter, case histories HYP/E, F and G are examples of this technique. The second is abreaction. Here the hypnotist helps the patient to 'act out' or 'work out' previously repressed emotions felt during some painful experience in the past. This is done by suggesting to the patient that they relive the experience while in a state of deep trance. Case histories HYP/H, I, J and K are examples of this technique.

Prohibitory Suggestion

Most prohibitory suggestion takes the form of posthypnotic suggestion, where the hypnotist suggests that things will be different when the subject wakes from trance. Sometimes the hypnotist will suggest to the subject that when they wake from trance all their painful symptoms will have disappeared (see case history HYP/E). At other times the suggestion will be made that a particular emotional difficulty will no longer exist when the trance state finishes (see case history HYP/G).

45

A variety of other commands can also be used ranging from suggestions about remembering or forgetting past events to suggestions about specific behaviour being triggered off by certain sights, sounds or smells. For instance, a would-be non smoker may be told that when he wakes from trance he will feel unwell every time he puts a cigarette in his mouth (see case history HYP/F). For insomniacs, the suggestion of sleep might be given when a certain tune is played on a tape recorder. Embarrassing if the tune plays at an inopportune moment.

The effectiveness of post-hypnotic suggestion usually depends on the depth of trance when given. Subjects in light trance may well not respond to this form of suggestion, whereas those in deep trance invariably do obey post-hypnotic suggestions. One interesting piece of research into the use of post-hypnotic suggestion came from a group of researchers and doctors who invited 14 people to help them investigate the treatment of stubborn or resistant warts with hypnosis. Of the 14 in the trial ten were hypnotisable to a level of at least medium trance and the rest were only able to gain light states of trance. Those participating were thought to be only lightly hypnotised if they did not respond to a simple post-hypnotic suggestion that they close the door of the laboratory when the hypnotist coughed. Of the ten who were properly hypnotisable, six were completely cured of their warts after about a dozen sessions of hypnosis using a post-hypnotic suggestion that their warts would gradually disappear. Of the remaining four, three were partially cured of their warts and one was completely unaffected. (For this and another corroborating report see Bibliography Nos. 13 & 14.)

While these prohibitory suggestions may appear to have some effect superficially, Sigmund Freud reckoned that when they were applied to problems of an emotional nature they usually did no more than, 'Cover up and gloss over something in the mental life.' Freud added that 'the use of suggestion in order to forbid the symptoms ... strengthens the repressions ... and leaves all the processes that have led to the formation of the symptoms unaltered.' Talking about the long-term effects of such suggestive treatment, Freud described it as not only being unreliable, but also transitory in its effects, often leading the patients into greater difficulties (see Bibliography No. 22 pages 502–504).

Whether we believe Freud's theories to be good or bad, his observations about the limitations of the use of the prohibitive suggestion during hypnosis are, I think, valid. However his humanist ideals prevented him from recognising and reporting the intrusion of evil spiritual forces during trance when it occurred.

Abreaction

In the next chapter case histories HYP/H, I and J all describe patients reliving some form of painful experience so as to allow powerful and previously repressed emotions to be expressed within the controlled environment of hypnotic trance. Called hypnotherapeutic abreaction, these experiences usually require quite a deep state of hypnotic trance before they can be embarked upon.

Abreactive techniques such as age regression and the recall of blurred memories are often used to treat a variety of problems. Most commonly, hypnotherapists like to use these methods in the treatment of psychosomatic disorders. These are physical illnesses which are thought to be caused by emotional imbalances and for which conventional medicine is usually only able to alleviate the symptoms, whereas hypnotherapy may claim to offer a cure. This is because the hypnotic trance is thought to provide an easy way of finding, and then resolving, any underlying emotional disturbances.

Occasionally a person can experience an event which later on is too painful even to consciously remember. Children who have been seriously abused often repress the memory so that when they grow up they do not actually recall any painful events in their childhood. Instead pleasant memories are interspersed with a general hazy blur.

One form of hypnotic abreaction consists of discovering these unconsciously stored recollections of traumatic events under trance in the hope that as sufferers relive their moments of extreme pain, they can express the appropriate emotion, anger, fear, etc. It is believed that the release of these repressed emotions is the key to the healing of some apparently incurable illnesses, such as rheumatic problems, asthma and eczema.

It is worth noting that this form of hypnotic abreaction, like all abreaction, often does no more than reopen a festering wound. It may well allow the release of emotional 'pus' but, in my opinion, it cannot really effect any lasting healing.

When we have been deeply hurt by others, it is my belief that true forgiveness is the only thing which can properly resolve any resentment or bitterness. From personal experience I am convinced that true forgiveness is always possible even when we feel that we cannot forgive or perhaps when we do not initially want to forgive. For as we turn to God (who loves and cares) by openly confessing our need, Jesus is then able to come in and heal the hurts and begin the process of forgiveness. Since this may, to begin with, involve a person becoming aware of a deep sense of anger at having been sinned against – something that may have previously been denied – some form of abreaction may have a place in helping people to deal with bitterness or resentment. But I believe that it is best to deal with this kind of difficulty in the context of Holy Spirit guided and Christ-centred prayer and counselling, and not hypnosis.

With age regression, people are hypnotised and then taken back year by year through their lives, with a view to uncovering emotional damage that needs resolving. So real is the regression possible under hypnosis that the hypnotised person may even mimic the sucking reflex of a baby or lose other normal adult reflexes and assume infant ones. This may seem fairly harmless, until hypnotists begin to suggest going beyond your early life and delving back into previous lives. These supposed 'past life' experiences sometimes seem quite authentic, but since the Bible directly contradicts the erroneous teaching of reincarnation (see Luke 16:19–31 and Hebrews 9:27), I must conclude that hypnotherapeutic age regression techniques are wide open to the influences of a fertile imagination or even demonic interference.

Despite this, I think that it is unwise to reject the fact that unremembered events in our very early childhood may cause difficulties for some people. Abortion, infant or child abuse, and other traumatic events in very early life can cause problems with feelings of rejection, guilt and anxiety, and subsequently may cause people to block out emotions that remind them of their past. This, in turn, may cause a stunting of normal happy development. Again, I believe, it is best to resolve this sort of difficulty through Christian counselling and prayer under the direction and in the power of the Holy Spirit.

Chapter 4

Case Histories Involving Hypnotherapy

In this chapter, ten case histories are given which indicate that hypnosis can cause serious problems even when it is carried out by a medically trained hypnotist. Whether these problems arise from our inadequate understanding of the human personality, or whether they are due to some interaction with the forces of spiritual evil is open to question. I believe that in the majority of these cases trance states have exposed the subjects to the influence of demonic agencies.

Examples of Lay Hypnosis

Case History HYP/C 'Just for Fun'

This example shows how children, in particular, can be vulnerable to occult powers when in a state of heightened suggestibility (i.e. trance). It is not the only one of its kind as I have come across similar cases. In the book *The Holy Spirit and You*, Dennis and Rita Bennett cite how a teenage girl's behaviour dramatically changed after a 'just for fun' exposure to hypnotism at a party. After hypnosis, the girl had a noticeable change of personality. She became unreachable by her parents and participated in serious misbehaviour, including car theft. At fourteen she was ministered to for deliverance and was released from the influence that a spirit had gained during hypnosis.

Case History HYP/D 'Depression Banished'

An account is available of a depressed and suicidal Christian lady who picked up a book highlighting the activity of oppressive spirits during hypnosis. She then remembered the time some years back when a well-meaning therapist had hypnotised her in order to recall an incident which had caused her mother's miscarriage.

She confessed this to the Lord, asking his forgiveness and immediately experienced considerable release. She was soon free of all need for medical treatment and testifies that her severe distress was satanic in origin, and related to her having been hypnotised twenty years previously by someone who had genuinely wanted to help her (see No. 17 of the Bibliography).

Case History HYP/E 'Costly Pain Relief'

This example is taken from Kurt Koch's book *The Devil's Alphabet*. I have cited it as an example of the removal of physical symptoms by a deceiving spirit operating during hypnosis. Some Christians may quite understandably disagree with this interpretation and believe it to be an example of how physical symptoms of pain can shift to an area of the personality, causing emotional difficulties instead.

Dr Koch told how he met a Christian whose mother had suffered from severe biliary colic (pain due to gall-stones). On one occasion when the pain became very severe, the family doctor was called in. Instead of giving a strong painkiller the doctor hypnotised the mother and effected relief within minutes. However, after this hypnotic treatment the mother's character completely altered. She developed an evil temper that at times bordered on madness. In these tantrums it was not uncommon for her to throw plates around the room, and on one occasion she tore some electric light fittings from the wall. The mother's children were in no doubt about what they thought of hypnosis; they were strongly opposed to it.

Dr Koch says that this was not just one isolated case, and incidents similar to this were often confessed to him in his counselling work.

Case History HYP/F 'Worse after Hypnosis'

An almost exactly similar case-history was reported to me by someone who lives in our local area. He was a Christian and was concerned at the change in a relative of his. The relative and his own daughter had gone for hypnotherapy to stop smoking. The daughter claimed to be unaffected by the trance induction and was not helped in the least to quit smoking. The relative, on the other hand, was quite deeply hypnotised and immediately afterwards felt sick at the prospect of smoking. But, though released from the compulsive desire to smoke, a considerable personality change occurred and he was unpredictably violent. In addition he began to experience severe pain in some of his joints.

Examples of Medical Hypnosis

Case History HYP/G 'From Spiders to Alcohol'

Another incident that Dr Koch relates in one of his many books on occult-associated activity involves what some might call the 'transference' of emotional problems during hypnosis. My own view is that this case is an example of how hypnosis worsened the spiritual oppression already evident in someone's life (see Luke 11:24–26).

This particular story concerned a woman who had a distressing spider-complex. Day and night she was tormented by seeing spiders all over the house; on the floors, on the walls and on the ceiling. Because no amount of soothing words seemed to help, she went to an eminent doctor for help. This doctor hypnotised her and then, when she was in trance, said, 'When you wake up you will not see any more spiders.'

This treatment was successful since she did not see spiders any more. Everything seemed successful until it emerged that she had become an alcoholic from the time of her hypnosis onwards. Instead of being tormented by visions of spiders, she was in the grip of alcohol. Similar experiences caused the doctor who had treated her to decide against the use of hypnosis, as he observed that the symptoms had altered, but there had been no effective deliverance from the root problem (see Bibliography No. 16 page 96).

The following case histories were published by an American doctor, also a hypnotherapist, in the *Journal of the American Medical Association* (see Bibliography No. 12).

Case History HYP/H 'Suicide!'

The first case history concerns a patient who had severe back pain. After surgery (Laminectomy) had failed to rectify matters, he was seen by a non-medically qualified hypnotherapist and under trance abreacted (see previous chapter) a painful experience. The back pain disappeared but the following week he committed suicide by jumping from an upper-storey window. The doctor who quoted this incident believed that the back pain masked a depressive illness which should have been dealt with first.

Case History HYP/I 'Sexual Problems'

An adolescent young man was admitted to a hospital for the surgical correction of a wry neck (torticollis). This is a condition in which the muscles on one side of the neck are more contracted than those of the other side and so the head is continually tilted one way. But before surgery he was put into hypnotic trance and abreacted a sexually traumatic experience. His wry neck immediately disappeared and the surgery he had expected to have was cancelled. However he began almost straight away to display exhibitionistic homosexual behaviour. The condition he was left with was worse than the first.

Case History HYP/J 'Bowel Problems'

This incident concerns a woman who had a fairly mild form of ulcerative colitis (a chronic bowel disease of unknown origin causing attacks of diarrhoea). This woman was hypnotised and under trance acted out an incestuous episode which took place when she was 5 to 6 years old with an older brother. As a result of this trance state experience she obtained relief from her ulcerative colitis symptoms. However, when this older brother died, about a month after the funeral, her old symptoms returned in a more severe form requiring her to be hospitalised.

Like the case history before, this abreaction of sexually traumatic experiences may well have been false. This is because other hypnotic abreactive experiences have sometimes involved what are called 'past life' events – or events that occurred in a previous life. Since all stories about 'past life' experiences are most likely either the result of a fertile imagination or the upshot of demonic interference, it is probably wise to question the origins and authenticity of stories arising from hypnotherapeutic abreaction.

Obviously all these case histories are a little extreme and are not very commonly reported. A medical Christian hypnotherapist based in Glasgow claimed to me on a BBC radio interview, that he had never known this sort of thing to happen to any of his patients. I do not question his claim, but I do wonder how much he had followed up the spiritual health of the clients whom he had hypnotised. He might have found that those who had been deeply affected by hypnosis had also become quite hardened to the message of God's love through Jesus Christ, or become vulnerable to unpredictable bouts of depression, temper, fear and confusion.

This was the case in my final case history concerning medical hypnosis.

Case History HYP/K 'Admitted to a Psychiatric Hospital'

Anne (not her real name) went to her family GP for help with weight reduction. She was finally referred to a therapist who was a medically trained counsellor and who regularly used hypnosis. During the four years of ensuing treatment Anne experienced most hypnotic techniques, including training in self-hypnosis, but nothing was effective in the long term. As a last resort the therapist decided to induce a deep trance and start abreactive questioning. Anne does not recall the experience but only remembers feeling very sick and retching. The counsellor judged this as a good sign and proceeded with the abreactive therapy but eventually had to terminate the trance state without any success.

Almost immediately after this trance state had been stopped Anne began to feel tired and acutely depressed, and was admitted to a local psychiatric hospital where she then slept for the next two days.

Later on Anne became a Christian and related to me that during this, her last, trance state experience she had felt very exposed to forces of spiritual evil. Had she known about the love and care of Jesus at that time she would never have agreed to be hypnotised.

An Example of Mind Control

Case History HYP/L 'Mind Control'

A more complete and rounded testimony of the occult movement in hypnosis comes from the life story of an American Jew, Sid Roth. In his book, *Something for Nothing* he vividly explains that what he innocently believed to be the harnessing of mental power was, in reality, the utilisation of demonic forces.

Searching for success, money and fame, Mr Roth came to practise what was called 'Mind control'. Effectively it involved a self-induced state of hypnotic trance in which he was told to imagine that he had a counsellor in his head. The trance state was induced by relaxation techniques and meditation, and the counsellor with whom Sid Roth became acquainted with in his head was able to diagnose illness, help him make money, predict the future and even guide him home when he was lost in a city. Even before he became a believer (in Jesus) and renounced such practices, he began to recognise the sinister powers behind this form of self-hypnosis that can lead people into life-destroying patterns of existence.

The change in his life began when Mr Roth started to chat with some colleagues who were Christians. Through the persistent testimony of these Gentile believers, he was released from a crippling web of fear and self-centredness as he started to trust Jesus in his life, and later on he was reunited with his wife and small child. As Jesus said,

> *'The thief* (Satan) *comes only to kill, steal and destroy, but I have come that they* (those who trust Jesus) *might have life and have it more abundantly.'*
>
> (John 10:10)

A similar story about mind control is told in the section on self-hypnosis at the end of this book (page 113). But this time the lady who relates the story seemed content with the powers that she had gained through self-hypnosis, even though the evidence for the involvement of spiritual evil in her case is quite strong.

Chapter 5

What the Bible Says About Hypnosis

The Ancients

Ever since ancient civilisations began to keep records, there has been almost without fail some mention of trance states. Babylonian or Persian cuneiform clay inscriptions mention them, Egyptian hieroglyphic writing on papyrus mention them, and ancient Greek, Chinese and Indian writings all record the use of the trance state in bringing healing. In particular, the Ebers papyrus (see page 60), which is over 3000 years old, mentions the trance state techniques used by Egyptian soothsayers and it appears that these have much in common with current hypnotic practices. Also the earliest Greek medical records describe how priests of the Aesculapian temples brought about miraculous healing through their ritual magic, by inducing trance-like conditions in worshippers. These healings were usually attributed to the goodness of some benevolent god who was represented by the mediating priest.

The Law Given to Moses

For the Christian valuable information about God's attitude to hypnosis can be gleaned from the way he instructed his people, Israel, to view the trance state

This is an example of the Ebers Papyrus discovered during the nineteenth century. Some of the passages contained within this book of scrolls written during the 15th century BC, describe ritual trance-inducing procedures that are very similar to those used by modern-day hypnotists.

practices of the ancient Canaanites (circa 1500 BC) when they invaded Canaan after forty weary years in the wilderness.

In the Bible we read that God enabled the 12 tribes of Israel to oust the Canaanites from the land given by promise to their forefather Abraham. Jericho's walls may have come crashing down and Israel may have even conquered giants as they cleared the land, but the battle of fidelity to God was just beginning. To ensure that his chosen people were not drawn away to the worship of idols, God gave strict instructions to Moses about how the Israelites were to view the old magico-religious practices of the Canaanites. In Deuteronomy chapter 18, beginning at verse nine, we find the following injunction.

> *'When you come into the land which the Lord your God gives you, you shall not learn to do* (follow) *after the abominations* (something that is detestable, even sinister and dangerous) *of those nations. There shall not be found among you anyone who makes his son or daughter to pass through fire* (as an offering to Molech), *anyone that uses divination, an observer of times* (? this is thought to be divination through 'reading' clouds), *a fortune-teller, a SPELL CASTER, a MAGIC CHARMER, anyone that consults a familiar spirit, a wizard or one inquiring of the dead. For all that do these things are an* **abomination** *to the Lord, and because of these abominations the Lord your God is driving them out before you.'*

Though most modern civilisations would be shocked at the thought of making children pass through fire as a sacrifice to Molech, somehow, very subtly the idols of our societies seem to be demanding the same, and we have abortion laws that allow countless little (unborn) lives to be wasted on the altar of so-called human compassion. Therefore when considering the relevance of these injunctions we need to look carefully at what was said and transpose it into our present day world.

Magic Charmers?

The word 'charmer', a translation of the first part of Deuteronomy 18:11 common to many English versions, is rather old fashioned and today usually means someone who impresses others with his or her intelligence, wit or beauty. The real meaning of this word as it is used in this passage of the Bible is obviously different.

The actual Hebrew words used to convey this meaning are *chober chaber* or *charmers of magic*. Strong's concordance suggests that an alternative translation of these words in the context of the passage in Deuteronomy involves the old English usage of the word 'to fascinate'. This word, in turn, is generally defined by dictionaries as 'to transfix by an irresistible mental power', or even 'to captivate'.

But the true nature of the charming and of the magic is only really found when you consider the root of the two words, which is *chabar*. This word generally implies a joining or uniting, probably best expressed by the phrase 'to make an alliance'. Some Hebrew wordbooks enlarge on this by citing the ancient practice of tying magic knots or tying up a person with magic. So the Hebrew word *chabar* conveys a sense of agreement or co-operation between the charmed and the charmer. Since hypnosis usually requires some form of agreed abdication of the mind in favour of the hypnotist, the Hebrew phrase *chober chaber* in Deuteronomy 18 is probably equally well translated as 'those who use their mental/psychic powers over some consenting party,' or even, 'those who hypnotise or charm either man or animals.'

A Hebrew scholar from the organisation Prayer for Israel examined this interpretation and concluded that although 'the Hebrew word "*chaber*" can't be literally translated into hypnosis ... the concept involved in gaining control over someone, after a false sleep is produced, is very much contained within the word.'

Another place in the Bible where the root word *chabar* is used to convey similar meaning is found in Psalm 58.

Here King David actually refers to the practice of snake charming (animal hypnosis) saying that the wicked are like the poisonous snake that blocks its ears rather than hear the magician's voice or the skilful snake charmer's (*chabar*) spells. Again here is an example where the activity of charming seems to be dependent on the co-operation of the party being charmed, therefore implying something rather similar to modern-day hypnosis.

Spell Casters?

The word *chabar* also carries the idea of spell-casting. This meaning is well illustrated in Isaiah's description of the judgement that was to come upon Babylon as found in Isaiah chapter 47. Verse 9 of this chapter refers to the numerous and powerful spells (*chabar*) that the Babylonians had developed. These spells were not used for aggressive purposes but are described, in verse 12, as being for the benefit of the people. The Babylonians thought (wrongly) that these spells would make them strong.

Just prior to the word 'charmers' (Hebrew root *chabar*) in the passage in Deuteronomy chapter 18 the word 'spell casters' (Hebrew root *Kisheph*) is written. The spell casters referred to here are sometimes described as enchanters and often had some role in dealing with health problems through magic. In Babylonian culture the sick often underwent surgery while these enchanters uttered their incantations. In short these spell casters were the witch doctors or soothsayers of ancient middle-eastern tribes.

Although it is not at first obvious, the modern equivalent of 'spells' when translated into medical jargon is what is known as 'post-hypnotic suggestions.' These are the suggestions that are implanted during trance and which are designed to alter a person's behaviour after the trance state has been terminated. So in old fashioned language we would say that a magician bewitched or charmed a person and cast a spell on him which set him free from his difficulty. But in today's language we would say that a hypnotherapist induced a state of relaxation and increased suggestibility in a patient (a hypnotic trance) and then implanted a post-hypnotic suggestion which changed his behavioural pattern. Therefore, although the overall transaction is exactly the same, i.e. a spell had been cast over someone who was in a trance, everything is dressed in a fine veneer of scientific jargon.

Some readers might think this interpretation of the act of post-hypnotic suggestion is too extreme. But Sigmund Freud wrote in a similar fashion when describing the basic form of hypnosis that he sometimes practised. All he did was to induce a trance in his subject (if he was able), and then implant a suggestion that the difficulty or symptoms of disease would stop. He then woke the patient from the trance state and occasionally found that some form of healing had occurred. As Quote 'J' in the Appendix indicates, Freud eventually regarded this type of post-hypnotic suggestion as 'unscientific activity' reminding him of 'magic incantations and hocus pocus'.

This similarity between spells and post-hypnotic suggestions is one of the reasons why a well known hypnotherapist wrote that the 'hypnotic procedures used by Egyptian soothsayers ... have a lot in common with current hypnotic practice' (see Bibliography No. 1). In view of this it is not difficult to link hypnotherapy with the activities of the 'magic charmers' and 'spell casters' of Deuteronomy chapter 18, and therefore see it as condemned by God.

Trance States in the New Testament

Coming forward in time to the era when the New Testament was written, we find that its writers directly refer to trance states. The Greek word for trance as found in the New Testament is *Ekstasis* meaning literally 'out of (*ek*), a standing (*stasis*)'. This implies an experience beyond the realm of the normal.

This type of experience is first mentioned when Peter

was about to announce the good news of Jesus Christ to Cornelius, the Gentile. Just before Peter agreed to go to Cornelius' home, he was staying at the house of Simon the tanner. About midday Peter went up on to the roof of the house to pray (Acts 10:10). Lunchtime was imminent and Peter was hungry. But before he could satisfy his hunger, a trance *'came upon'* Peter (Greek literal translation) and it was while he was in this trance that Peter had a vision from God. In this vision Peter saw a large sheet, like a sail strung up to dry, being lowered from heaven, and in it were all kinds of animals, reptiles and birds, both clean and unclean (according to Jewish law). After this he heard a voice saying to him, *'Get up, Peter, kill and eat.'*

But Peter said, 'not so, Lord, for I have never eaten anything that is common or unclean.'

This vision occurred three times and when the great sheet had finally been taken back to heaven, Peter began to think about what it all meant.

This form of visionary trance also happened to Paul while he was praying in the temple just after his conversion (Acts 22:17). Paul himself relates that during this experience the Lord instructed him to leave Jerusalem, telling him also that the Pharisaic Jews would not listen to his testimony. Paul tried to reason with the Lord because he wanted to convert those with whom he had once collaborated in the extermination of Christians. But the Lord interrupted him and reiterated what he had first commanded Paul to do, adding that Paul would be sent to the non-Jewish nations who had not heard the gospel.

Spiritual Interaction

Probably the most valuable thing that we can learn from these New Testament passages is that trance states allow communication or interaction of a spiritual nature. Men and women are souls who possess both a body and a spirit. With their bodies they relate to the material world and with their spirits they communicate with the spiritual world.

In these examples of trance states from the New Testament both Peter and Paul were interacting with the spiritual part of their souls. They heard the words of Jesus not physically with their ears, but spiritually. Peter did not see his vision actually with his eyes, but he saw what the Lord wanted to show him through the perception of his spirit.

Elsewhere in the Bible Ezekiel, Isaiah, and John in their respective visions did not undergo physical experiences but rather saw, heard and felt things with their spiritual senses. John, for example, explained the context of his revelation of Jesus Christ, as found in the last book of the Bible, by saying that he was *'in the spirit'* (Revelation 1:10 and Revelation 4:2).

If these men of God were, through a trance state, made more open to experiences of a spiritual nature initiated by God, then it follows that humanly induced trance states may also expose a soul to spiritual interaction. The danger exists, therefore, that during an hypnotic trance, someone may be laid open to spiritual forces which are occult and which seek to destroy the lives of men and women rather than build them up. In my view the history of hypnosis seems to indicate that humanly induced trance states do permit interaction with occult forces much in the same way that séances enable men and women to communicate with the spiritual world. Perhaps this is why mediums at séances so often enter trance states in order to make contact with evil spirit beings. (For more detail, see Table 3.)

No Ritual

The next thing to notice about the trance states recorded in the Bible is that no ritual activity (i.e. mantras, repetitive actions or chanting, etc.) is mentioned. Peter and Paul did not premeditate the trance they fell into, it just happened. In the same way Ezekiel usually introduced his visionary trance experiences by saying that *'the hand of the Lord God fell upon me'* (Ezekiel 1:3, 8:1 and 40:1).

In humanly induced trance states ritual activity is

Table 3
Ways in Which Harmful Spiritual
Experiences May Be Induced

This table attempts to show that hypnosis and other associated trance induction techniques are just one of the many ways in which harmful spiritual or mystical experiences may be induced. In nearly all these, mental passivity or drug induced mental passivity is the common factor linking them and it is this that opens the door of the personality and allows some sort of inter-action with the forces of spiritual evil.

1. Religious:
(a) Yoga
(b) Mind emptying meditation techniques associated with world religions (e.g. Transcendental Meditation) and the martial arts
(c) Idolatry or the worship of false gods
(d) Christian Science

2. Drug Induced:
(a) Uncontrolled use of opium derivatives (e.g. morphine)
(b) Uncontrolled use of barbiturates (e.g. phenobarbitone)
(c) Other drugs like alcohol or LSD

3. Hypnosis:
(a) Ordinary trance induction
(b) Self hypnosis
(c) Autogenic Training
(d) Mind control

4. Occult Related Activities:
(a) Overtly occult activities like mediumship or 'channelling'
(b) Occult based media events (e.g. the film *The Exorcist*)
(c) Fantasy games (e.g. Dungeons and Dragons)

5. Therapies Based on Ritual:
(a) Acupuncture and associated therapies (e.g. Acupressure, reflexology)
(b) Some aspects of Chiropractic and Osteopathy
NB: These therapies may not actually cause trance states. Instead they seem to induce 'trance like' states (see Chapter 8).

6. Stress Control Techniques:
(a) Relaxation tapes, especially those with a 'New Age' emphasis.
(b) Visualisation.
(c) Biofeedback.

---

absolutely essential. Whether it is staring at a coin or a pinpoint of light, or whether it involves the rhythmical stroking of an area of skin, all hypnotists, both medically trained and occult orientated, use some form of ritual to induce a trance state in their subjects.

No Loss of Free Will

Another facet that characterises trance states in the Bible is that those men of God who were privileged to experience these unique expressions of the heart of God, were never in any way deprived of their ability to respond normally to the things God was showing them. For example, during his visions of the great sheet being lowered from heaven, Peter disobeyed what he recognised as the Lord's voice three times. Paul similarly tried, while in trance, to persuade the Lord to let him stay just a little while longer in Jerusalem so that he could have a better chance of telling the Pharisaic Jews that Jesus was really the Messiah. John, in Revelation chapter 5, verse 4, is found weeping during his visionary experience because no man was found worthy to open the book of the seven seals. Further on in chapter 19 he is rebuked by an angel for inappropriate worship.

This kind of ordinary response during trance, as mentioned in the Bible, is rarely encountered during humanly-induced trance states. In fact most research indicates that someone who is hypnotised is not able to respond normally but instead waits for instructions from the hypnotist about what to do and say (see Quote 'K' of the Appendix).

Mystical Experiences

During the research that has been done into deep humanly induced trance states, subjects who have delved into these hidden areas have sometimes returned to consciousness with stories about mystical experiences. These may include the separation of soul from body and the subsequent travelling of what is called the 'astral' soul to distant parts of the universe. It may also include more nebulous things like feeling at one with the universe and a sense of gaining knowledge that is incommunicable (see the Appendix Quote 'E').

Curiously, experiences like these are mentioned quite openly but with a little mystery, in the closing part of Paul's second letter to the Corinthians. In 2 Corinthians chapter 12, verses 1–4, Paul talks of visions and revelations of the Lord (verse 1). He then relates that he knew a man in Christ (i.e. a Christian, possibly himself) who was caught up into the third heaven. In ancient Jewish thought, the first heaven usually referred to the space immediately above our planet, the second heaven referred to the rest of the universe, and the third heaven was where God and his angels were. Paul was unsure whether this man was whisked away to this place with or without his body, in other words he was unsure whether it was simply a spiritual experience or perhaps, because it seemed so real, that he actually went there in his body. Whatever the real state of this man, he went to Paradise or the third heaven and heard things which he was not permitted to speak of.

I have no doubt that this was a mystical experience. However this was a vision or a revelation given to him by the Lord (verse 1). Mystical experiences in hypnotic trance, on the other hand, are counterfeits engendered by Satan, and are contrary to the real revelations which the Lord of heaven and earth (Jesus) delights to give to his children through the Holy Spirit, who is poured out on all who will receive him.

An example of a modern day, God initiated, mystical trance state experience happened to Demos Shakarian, the founder of the movement 'The Full Gospel Business Men's Fellowship International'. In his book *The Happiest People on Earth*' he describes how God gave him a vision of the way that this movement would radically affect the world. During his encounter with God, Demos Shakarian recalls that it began as he entered his living room having just finished a late night snack with his wife and a friend. Suddenly he felt forced to the floor until he lay prostrate on his patterned red carpet. Then his awareness of time and space left him and he heard God lovingly challenge him. He responded to what the Lord was saying to him and his spirit was lifted up out of his body to a place somewhere above the earth. He saw the earth spinning below him and at the same time he was shown faces of those living in the countries that passed before him. The faces were terrifyingly lifeless and miserable but as the earth spun a second time everything changed and joy and vitality filled the hearts of those he saw. After this the vision ended. It had lasted about three and a half hours. Both he and his wife, who was also present, believed that this trance state vision was confirmation of the rightness of the ministry that the Shakarians were about to start. Time has proved the correctness of the vision and affirms that God still speaks to people through such trance state experiences.

The occult counterfeit of this kind of spiritual encounter is what is known as 'astral projection' and this is commonly reported to happen during humanly induced trance states. The person who, by hypnosis, taps into the powers of his or her unregenerate human spirit or any opportunistic satanic spirits, may well have similar experiences to men and women who look to Jesus the Messiah. However, they are not the positively life-changing events which God intends them to be. To participate in mysticism under hypnotic trance often involves being lured deeper into practices that become more and more occult in nature, possibly leading to dabbling with witchcraft and other ungodly pursuits.

Maybe the most authoritative testimony concerning the true nature of mystical experiences within hypnotic trance can be found in Rabindranath R. Maharaj's book, *Death of a Guru*. The author, who turned to Jesus after zealously practising Hinduism, clearly explains that trance states induced either by yogic meditation, conventional hypnotic trance induction or the drug LSD can produce mystical experiences. These may involve astral projection to distant planets and worlds or the confronting of images representative of Hindu deities (in reality only demonic deceptions).

Mr Maharaj also clearly delineates between the fearful encounters he had with satanic powers who masqueraded as Hindu gods (as experienced in yogic trance) and the incident when Jesus appeared to him one night for the purpose of loving encouragement.

We need never deny the reality of supernatural experiences, but as people who have found the true God, we must simply trust Jesus to be the sole initiator of mystical experiences that are truly edifying. All other experiences, especially those produced by the deliberate induction of some form of trance state are as Mr Maharaj says, simply 'opening up one's mind to the domination of evil spirits' (page 159). Furthermore it needs to be added that 'waiting on God' in an utterly passive state of mind can lay a person open to deceitful visions and oppressive experiences. Many erroneous Christian teachings have started up when Christians have gone off the rails after a vision during passive meditation. Perhaps this is best illustrated by the heresy of Gnosticism which began to infiltrate Christian communities as early as 90 AD. Among the many errors of Gnosticism, it taught that men and women were set free and redeemed when they received some special and secret knowledge. This knowledge was often sought through mysticism.

Medieval Christian Mystics

If we were to summarise the last few pages, we would have to say that all humanly contrived mystical experiences can expose us to an evil spiritual influence. To put it another way, unless God initiates a trance state experience then it is likely to cause trouble.

When we examine the lives and teachings of those Christian men and women who, down the centuries, have actively sought mystical experiences, the misguiding influence in humanly induced mystical trance states becomes more obvious.

Many mystics have been well respected Christian leaders and writers (e.g. St. Francis of Assisi) and yet sometimes we find that their teachings contain unscriptural elements which have distracted other believers away from a pure faith and dependence on Jesus as their Saviour. For example, many medieval mystics encouraged an unwarranted and unbiblical amount of asceticism (self denial of human needs like food, sleep, human comfort or companionship). Although Paul, in his letter to the Colossians, encourages his readers to *'put to death ungodly desires'*, he also warns against those who promote self-imposed rigour of devotion, and delight in self-humiliation and severity of discipline of the body (see Colossians 2:23). Maybe one of the reasons for Paul's warning was that he realised that self-orientated ascetic activity can increase the likelihood of trance states. Aspiring Hindu gurus and Buddhist monks are taught this, and deliberately go into cold and rigorous conditions, without food and adequate clothing, in order to increase their spiritual potency, usually through trance state experiences.

The foundation of Christian mysticism during the middle ages was what was called 'methodical (step by step) contemplation' or 'mental prayer'. This may sound quite acceptable but the methods used sometimes encouraged mind emptying activities which are recognised as reliable ways of inducing trances. As a result of these meditational methods, Teresa of Avila, Catherine of Genoa and others, claimed to have had mystical experiences, the pinnacle of which was the 'ecstatic state of spiritual marriage'. Like much of their teaching, such ideas sound very pious but there is no scriptural mandate for them. This is not surprising because, at that time, papal decree prevented most people from reading the Bible. Teresa also experienced a number of other manifestations like levitation, terrors, sharp pains, dislocations of bones, lack of feeling and coma. She estimated that prayer could be judged by what phenomena accompanied it. Because of their mystical experiences Teresa of Avila, Julian of Norwich and many others were regarded as slightly exclusive, and so whatever they taught carried greater authority despite sometimes being dangerously erroneous. Sadly, a cult-like following attended these mystics and caused serious divisions among the believers (cf 1 Corinthians 1:10–13).

Another famous so called 'Christian' mystic was the Dominican friar Meister Eckhart. He began to have a profound influence on German Christianity during the 14th century but his teachings were not orthodox, because he advocated a rather pantheistic view of divine nature (i.e. God is everything and everything is God). Although Meister Eckhart recanted these beliefs on his deathbed, the modern day 'New Age' movement strongly encourages a similarly erroneous (Hindu based) attitude to God, sometimes referring back to Eckhart's early writings.

One recent example of how the Christian mystic can be led astray is Thomas Merton. Having embraced the Catholic faith he went into a Trappist monastery in Kentucky. He lived there in increasing seclusion, and spent the last years of his life in a cabin in the woods from which he only emerged to eat meals and collect fresh water. Sadly during this time he began to imbibe Buddhist thought, and when he left on a trip to Thailand he had all but lost his Christian faith. Tragically he was killed in the East while attending a conference on Christianity and Buddhism.

In conclusion, I believe it is fair to say that actively seeking mystical experiences for whatever reason can expose men and women to trance states and misleading experiences. Cardinal Newman, the famous Anglican scholar who converted to Catholicism, remarked that mysticism 'begins in mist and ends in schism'. Furthermore it is vital for Christians to realise that biblical meditation never involves any sort of mind emptying technique. In contrast, when referring to meditation, the Bible always implies some element of 'chewing the cud'. It talks of ruminating or musing over God, his love, his laws, his creation, and the wonderful things that he has done for those who trust him (see Psalm 104:34, Psalm 119:97, Psalm 1:2, Joshua 1:8, Psalm 143:5, Psalm 77:12). This is important since there are some who advocate meditation as a way of relaxing, but usually it has an eastern mystical flavour.

Psychic Powers

We have already mentioned that hypnosis makes it easier for people to tap into the mysterious powers of their own human spirit as well as those of the hidden world of spiritual evil. These powers of our human spirit are usually called 'psychic' powers. People who exercise these psychic abilities can predict the future, unnaturally discern what others are thinking, and see things which are normally hidden. Andrew Taylor Still, the founder of Osteopathy, not only foresaw future events (e.g. the result of naval battles in the Spanish/American war of 1898) but was also said to be able to diagnose what was wrong with his patients with only a very brief examination. A.T. Still believed that the mind could be trained to see beneath the surface of the skin in the same way that X-rays can reveal hidden structures. Although Still was keenly interested in spiritualism, he claimed that his extraordinary powers were purely psychic.

Many Christians seem to regard psychic abilities as neutral. They do not believe that these abilities invoke the forces of the evil spiritual realms, neither do they believe

Since psychic activity does not involve someone intentionally invoking the spiritual powers of good or evil, it is regarded as neutral. However because of the effects of original sin 'when man throws himself into neutral, he does not drift closer to God, he drifts farther away from God.'

(Quote from *Examining the Cults* by Harold J. Berry)

that the power of God is being called on. Therefore, like artistic talent or business acumen or musical aptitude, psychic abilities are thought to be just another gifting of the human soul. But the Bible teaches that although psychic powers do not involve someone intentionally invoking either the power of God or Satan, they are nevertheless unhelpful. Let us see how.

The Bible says that in the beginning God made men and women to be living souls capable of having a relationship with himself (Genesis 2:7). Although, like man, the animals were also given the breath of life their ability to relate to God (or spiritually) is, I believe, rather limited. Apart from the instance where Balaam's donkey saw the angel of the Lord about to slay his master and stopped, and the time when a great fish swallowed up Jonah at God's command, animals are not described as being able to relate to God. Instead the Scriptures teach that man (male and female) is created in the image of God and therefore differs from the animals in that he has been given the ability to have spiritual relationship with God. This relationship is fully endorsed with the privilege of choice, and so men and women can choose whether they want to interact with God or with those beings that hate God.

In the beginning the man and the woman were, as we are now, living souls with bodies to interact with the physical world, and spirits to interact with the spiritual. When the time came for the man and the woman to shed their spiritual innocence, Satan made sure that he was in on the act to deceive and beguile where possible. In one sense he succeeded because the man and the woman chose to desire independence from God based upon lies, instead of dependence on God and obedience to what he had commanded.

Spiritually, therefore, Adam and Eve began a race of people who desire to be gods in their own right (Genesis 3:5) and who also have a natural disposition towards going against what God has commanded. Roughly this is what may be termed 'original sin'. This condition means that every time men and women attempt to exercise the psychic or spiritual side of their personalities, they develop their independence from God and nurture an unseen alliance with Satan. If we believe that psychic activity is neutral, we must also understand that 'when man throws himself into neutral, he does not drift closer to God, he drifts farther away from God.'

Some Christians believe that because we have spiritually 'died with Christ' and risen with him also, then the bias towards evil in psychic activity has been dealt with. This belief misses out the fact that we can only live uprightly before God as we continually look to him and not ourselves. Psychic powers are always based on man's desire to be free of any dependence on God and are therefore never pleasing to him. So, like other aspects of our carnal nature (i.e. envy, strife, pride), we need to put to death any desire to use psychic abilities so that our spirits can become subject to the Holy Spirit and the empowering which he brings.

Faith *v*. Suggestion

Whenever scientists attempt to belittle the miracles of Jesus they usually use the argument that Jesus was simply employing suggestion and trance state phenomena to accomplish what he wanted. The feeding of the five thousand, they say, was simply an example of mass hysteria where Jesus used the suggestion of the hallucination of food, to convince his followers that they had eaten a big meal of bread and fish. While any honest appraisal of the accounts of the feeding of the multitudes by Jesus will reveal the error of this kind of humanist argument, observers of modern day religious phenomena may regard suggestion, and not God, as the reason why some so-called miracles occur. Sadly in some cases they may be right.

Very often the modern day evangelistic/healing meeting is geared to inspire faith by raising the group expectation that God will move to touch those who need him. Although some healers/evangelists attempt to reduce the possibility of an unbalanced response to suggestion in a highly charged expectant religious audience, it is often extremely difficult to do so without also undermining genuine faith. Enthusiastic singing and impassioned preaching not only stir hearts to respond to God but may also cause vulnerable and needy people to react to the impulse of suggestion. How many of us have been impelled forward to the altar rail with the words of the preacher ringing in our ears only to find that our immediate need, whether physical or spiritual, is not met and we return to our seats and homes disappointed. I personally found that the sight of some respected leader kneeling at the altar rail was a very powerful suggestive trigger that frequently caused me to override what the Holy Spirit was saying and respond inappropriately. I feel sure that God works all these things out for our benefit if we continue to trust him, but Christian speakers need to be reminded of the suggestive power that they have when they address large gatherings.

I was recently reminded of the repercussions of allowing this sort of suggestive mechanism to take over in an evangelistic meeting. During a house group meeting a number of us began discussing the 'morning after' responses of those who had gone forward after the altar calls at a large tent crusade. It appeared that nearly everyone who had gone forward did not want to speak to the person who came round to follow up their response. British reserve notwithstanding it seems that the speaker's fame and his eloquence had, with the effects of a large crowd, been the reason they had gone to the front.

We need to be clear that evangelistic response and healing 'in Jesus' name' do not require the power of suggestion to make them happen. It is sometimes apparent that we are falling into the trap of trying to create a frenzied atmosphere of praise in the hope that the Holy Spirit will be more inclined to move in power. Spiritualists need to resort to hearty singing to get their séances moving but God is looking for the inward worship of our hearts and this may or may not be expressed in fervent praise. Also the Bible teaches that we are saved (and healed) not because we deserve to be saved or healed, but as a gift in the form of faith because we have heard God speak (and not just some famous evangelist).

Like salvation, healing is a gift and it does not need to be struggled for but received, and once received it cannot then be lost any more than a chunk of bread can be lost once it has been swallowed. Like the woman who had the chronic problem of bleeding (Mark 5), those who are healed by Jesus reach out in faith but it is God's power that meets them and heals them. The ensuing results can be seen on X-ray or checked by blood tests, and do not require further belief to sustain them.

Chapter 6

The History of Hypnosis

The Old Testament Influence

While the use of trance states to bring about healing flourished in the mainly occult cultures of the ancient world, a radical change began to take place in Europe after the Roman Empire officially embraced Christianity in about 300 AD. Roman lawmakers started to create laws modelled on those found in the Old Testament which banned anything to do with the occult. In this way trance induction was effectively outlawed because it had always been rather intimately associated with the pagan rituals of ancient cultures.

All over Europe, wherever Roman 'Canon Law' was adopted, this Judaic influence began to appear within the legal systems. In Britain, when Augustine converted Ethelbert of Kent around 600 AD, there was an immediate refashioning of the existing legal system according to the tenets of Roman Canon law. In Britain, as in many European countries, the influence of the Bible through the organisation of Roman law slowly began to confine the trance state to the domain of druids, magicians and witches.

And there it stayed for many centuries until around 1400 AD and the advent of the Christian revival known as the Reformation. As this move of the Holy Spirit began to influence national governing bodies, laws and penalties for 'bewitching' or 'enchanting' (as trance induction was known) became more strict. Most historians agree that the Reformation caused Christian men and women to become more aware of their adversary, the devil, and in many European countries which professed to be Christian, this led to an aggressive legal campaign against those who were involved in the occult.

In Britain there was a strong feeling that if a nation permitted witchcraft within its boundaries, then God's blessing would be prevented. Major catastrophes like the Black Death (1348–9) and the Great Plague of 1665, often fuelled the emotions behind this conviction, and the penalty for those convicted of sorcery was harsh, with unrepentant witches either being drowned or burnt at the stake. But wherever the law is executed without understanding excesses are bound to creep in, and by the sixteenth and seventeenth century some local judges in Britain were quite unbalanced over the issue. This social imbalance also transferred to the then new world (USA), and created witchhunts among the mainly Puritan communities, the best known of which (the Salem witchhunt) was immortalised by Arthur Miller in his play 'The Crucible'.

Magnetism

It was around the time of these American witchhunts that the seeds of change were planted. Although communities were glad to be free of any oppressive grip that witches had over them, there were also some notable miscarriages of justice. Ordinary people, who did not like what they saw in these savage abuses of the legal system, began to try to explain the paranormal in terms of natural laws. During this re-examination of the supernatural one of the most popular theories to emerge was that of magnetism, or more correctly 'Animal Magnetism'.

The concept of animal magnetism has its roots in the astrology of the middle ages and grew from the need to reconcile the astronomical discoveries of Kepler and Gallileo with the popular view that the position of the planets and stars affected life events.

It was also believed that unseen forces emanating from the planets influenced other facets of human life. The well-known seventeenth century herbalist, Nicolas Culpeper, based all his remedies on what he felt were the relationships between the planets and herbs. Like many others he supported a theory that was first put forward by the Swiss occultist, Paracelsus. This said that everything in nature, whether animal, vegetable or mineral was somehow connected to the movement of the planets. Just as the moon and the sun create the tides which ebb and flow on our shores, it was thought that an unseen fluid pervaded the universe which affected human health according to the movement of the planets. Since magnetism was an unseen, but quite obvious power within nature, Paracelsus suggested that magnetism was responsible for such psychic gifts as telepathy or thought transference. He also attributed the ability to bewitch, enchant or fascinate a person, as usually encountered in witchcraft, to some unseen magnetic fluid coming from the enchanter.

Interestingly, electricity was also used as an explanation for the effects of hypnosis, particularly in North America during the nineteenth century. But, like magnetism, theories based around electricity were soon abandoned since too many inconsistencies were discovered which seemed to indicate that spiritual or mental, and not physical, forces were at work.

Greatraks

In these turbulent times for those involved in anything out of the ordinary, one man succeeded in walking the tightrope between the anti-witchcraft lobby, and those exploring the paranormal. His name was Valentine Greatraks. In the middle of the seventeenth century, just after the English civil war, this wealthy Irish landowner, suddenly discovered that he had a gift of healing. His methods involved either just touching a person or more often stroking the skin of the subject, but his power was such that quite often when Greatraks 'stroked' sick people they were healed. Curiously a number of other phenomena occurred during these healing encounters. Some people fainted or went into convulsions and coma, and others had experiences of healing that can only be described as weird. A London man went to Greatraks one day with severe shoulder pain. Greatraks stroked his shoulder and 'allured' the pain down his arms and into his fingers, but found that the man's fingers then went numb. Interested onlookers thrust pins deeply into the man's fingers but he did not flinch. Greatraks stroked his fingers again and he immediately cried out in pain because of the pins, but not the shoulder problem.

Perhaps if Greatraks had been less wealthy, he would have been burnt as a witch, but somehow his prestige and generous integrity gave him the plausibility which saved him from the folk who declared his work to be devilish. Greatraks was reported to be a God-fearing, sensible man, but we cannot confirm that his power was divinely inspired because he never stated that he trusted in Jesus Christ as Lord. More importantly he never said that Jesus, through the Holy Spirit, was the author of the healing which he offered. Instead Greatraks believed that his healings were due to the fact that disease and pain were mainly caused by demonic powers, which he had the gift to be able to cast out.

The rhythmical stroking of the skin has in the past been used by others to induce therapeutic trance states. It was successfully employed some two centuries later by the Scotsman, James Esdaile, to induce hypnotic trance anaesthesia in patients on whom he was about to perform extremely painful surgical procedures. Therefore it is very likely that Greatraks, in his capacity as healer, was inducing trance states in his patients from which they often emerged cured of their particular problems. But Great-raks was not always successful, in particular, on the occasion when he was asked to give a demonstration to King Charles II.

Miracles?

Ever since the New Testament times those who believe in Jesus have rightly assumed a responsibility to pray and care for those who are sick. Jesus implied that healing and deliverance was as vital as our daily bread (Mark 7:27), adding that healing was one of the signs which would follow those who believed on him (Mark 16:18). Paul and the early disciples proved this to be true, and James encouraged those who were sick to go to the elders of their church for prayer and anointing with oil. Obviously miraculous healing is something that believers need to look to God for, but we must also be wary of the counterfeit.

Like counterfeit money, counterfeit Christian healing looks almost exactly the same as the real thing but it is worthless and dangerous to handle. Also counterfeit healing comes in all sorts of packaging, but underneath the religious veneer lies idolatry, and possibly the induction of some form of trance state.

One example of this counterfeit religious healing is when people visit a shrine or Church and ask to touch some venerated relic from the past. The Roman Catholic tradition has always been fertile ground for this kind of healing experience. Bede in his *History of the English Church and People* (700 AD), wrote quite often about healings connected with relics attributed to certain saints. One example cited by Bede involved a young man who had a tumour on one of his eyelids. During his stay in a monastery the young man was shown some of the remains of St. Cuthbert, and when he applied a few strands of the saint's hair to his tumour it disappeared miraculously. Although Bede generally accredits this healing to the goodness of God, he also venerates St. Cuthbert and his relics to a degree that he loses sight of the suffering of Jesus which made all divine healing possible. Consequently people began to trust the memory and relics of those who have been saved and not the Saviour himself. In this way idolatry creeps in under a religious disguise and allows the forces of spiritual evil to become involved with human life and produce counterfeit healing in a believer's life. Perhaps the key ingredient to this involvement is the induction (often unintentional) of some kind of trance state.

Another example of trance state healing may occur when people make a special pilgrimage to a shrine associated with a saint or Mary. Although there is sometimes no obvious loss of normal consciousness, as is common in hypnosis, these visits by pilgrims or religious people to holy shrines have all the ingredients for successful trance state experiences. For instance, there is usually a period of pre-conditioning prior to the visit during which time the imagination and belief can be fuelled with stories about previous miracles. During the visit itself there is often some form of build-up ritual, and finally there is the mental distraction as the subject concentrates on the sanctity of the saint or the beauty of the shrine that he or she is visiting. All through history, associated with many religious beliefs, there are instances of this kind of healing involving some form of trance state. Although some of the trance state ingredients may not be wrong in themselves, Scripture generally teaches that miracles of God through the activity of the Holy Spirit must primarily bring glory to Jesus. The miraculous happenings which occur in some religious settings neither bring glory to Jesus nor do they cause people to begin trusting him.

A good example of this kind of healing started in 1720 in the St. Medard area of France. Roman Catholic pilgrims began to converge on the tomb of François of Paris, since healings were said to happen at the place where this venerated Roman Catholic layman was buried. The healing process was usually accompanied by convulsions, dissociation (trance states and fainting) and other ecstatic manifestations. Along with the healings it was found that some visitors to this site, who went into these ecstatic (trance) states, could be cut with a knife or burnt with fire without suffering injury or pain. Marie Souet, for instance, was suspended in a sheet above a raging fire for about half an hour but neither she nor the sheet were in any way affected by the flames which lapped around her.

This sort of immunity to the normal effects of fire indicates that the St. Medard phenomena were not just 'mind over matter' experiences but instead were spiritually influenced happenings brought about by the trance states of those who participated. The activity of evil spirits is, I believe, being invoked in a similar way to protect the feet, bodies and clothing of entranced firewalkers or 'coal-strollers' in India and other Asian countries. These examples are simply counterfeits of the miraculous power of God that are made possible because trance states provide an open invitation for evil spirits to participate in human life. The real thing can be found in the Bible, in the book of Daniel where we find the spirit of God protecting Shadrach, Meshach and Abednego from the harmful effects of fire while their captors were killed just by approaching the fiery furnace (see Daniel chapter 3). These three men of God did not require a trance state to invoke God's amazing protection. Instead all they needed was their faith and a love for God and his commands.

Lourdes

What happened at St. Medard carried on for just under a decade and then faded and was forgotten, but re-emerged somewhere else in another format. One of the recent religious disguises of this manifestation of trance state power is the 'Lourdes' experience. Catholics from the world over flock to this little French town on the Spanish border in the hope that the Virgin Mary will smile on them and give them healing. While I do not want to demean the obvious sincerity of these people, it is my belief that much of the healing which occurs is not from God, since small gains in physical health are often accompanied by an increased bondage to the idolatry of Mary worship.

Having said this, some of the 'certified' healings at Lourdes may be genuine because they are accredited to Jesus. Earlier this century a Belgian man was healed of an advanced and severe form of tuberculosis. Although he depended on Mary as a substitute mother figure, his own having died in his early youth, he believed in Jesus and firmly maintained that it was Jesus who had healed him. This genuine miracle does not confirm the Marian traditions of Lourdes, instead it shows how the Holy Spirit is sometimes pleased to work even when there are barriers. For, like many Roman Catholic believers today, this Belgian man used to come to Jesus through, what I believe to be, a misguided and improper worship of Mary (see Footnote).

Footnote
The visions of Bernadette Soubirons in 1858 at Lourdes in which she claims she saw the virgin Mary were probably occult apparitions. As I understand it, the Bible prohibits any communication between the dead and the living. This is plain from the incident where Samuel was called up against his will by the witch of Endor (1 Samuel 28). Also in the story of Lazarus and the rich man, the latter's request to return from the dead to warn his family was denied by Abraham (Luke 16:19–31). There are some exceptions, but these are extraordinary one-off events like the transfiguration when Moses and Elijah were seen talking with Jesus (see also Matthew 27:52). Even though Mary was a blessed woman who was full of faith, she was, like us, someone who needed to trust Jesus for her salvation. However special her calling in this life, her so-called appearances in Lourdes, Fatima and more recently in Medjugorje do not seem to be in line with the Bible's ban on communication between the living and the dead.

Gassner

About thirty years after the healings at St. Medard in France (i.e. 1760), Europe was again confronted with yet more puzzling manifestations of healing. This time it was the ministry of a Swiss Roman Catholic priest called Johann Gassner. Like Greatraks, Gassner, through his own personal experience with health problems, came to believe that some disease, both physical and mental, could be caused by demonic powers. The cure, therefore, lay not with medical interference but with the expulsion of the demons causing the disease. Though Gassner attempted at all times to actually identify the troubling spirit before he expelled it from a sick body, he became known as a healer whose methods often involved convulsions, comas, trance states, fainting and manifestations of strange tongues.

Since a number of leading evangelists today base their ministry on ideas similar to Gassner's it is worth noting that there is only limited scriptural support for the theory that demonic possession is the main cause of sickness. Of the twelve incidents of demonic expulsion recorded in the

---

What seems to cast further suspicion over the 18 or 19 appearances at Lourdes, is that Bernadette Soubirons claimed the apparition called itself the 'Immaculate Conception'. Coming from an uneducated peasant girl this was seen to be a miracle in itself since the Papal Bull about the immaculate conception had been proclaimed by Pope Pius IX less than four years previously and was only known about in the higher echelons of the Roman Catholic system. The whole idea that Mary was herself conceived by God, making her sinless, is definitely not substantiated or even implied by Scripture. This erroneous teaching induces many Catholics to venerate Mary as though she was almost on a par with God, and Lourdes is littered with statues of Mary who is worshipped and appealed to by the thousands of pilgrims who visit Lourdes each year. This, despite the fact that Christians are exhorted through Scripture not to create and worship any sculpted statue or graven image (Exodus 20:3–5).

New Testament five were said to have been linked with sickness. Of these five the chief manifestation of ill-health was that of blindness or dumbness (the inability to speak). In addition to this, Jesus and the apostles spent a much larger amount of time simply healing the sick. However it is possible that sickness and some form of demonic activity are linked, because Peter declared in Acts chapter 10 verse 38, that Jesus '. . . *went about doing good and healing all those who were oppressed by the devil.*'

It is quite likely that some of what happened at Gassner's meetings was not the upshot of genuine exorcism but simply the effects of group hysteria giving rise to trance state manifestations. Sadly similar occurrences may be going on in some modern day charismatic meetings where people fall to the ground. Some people collapse, not through the power of God, but because others are falling down and the ritual of falling over is a signal for the suggestion or reassurance of healing. Perhaps without knowing it needy people believe that if they fall over, then it is more likely that God has moved to heal or deliver.

Sometimes those being prayed for will be instructed to 'let go' and relax because they are somehow thought to be resisting God's desire to move in their lives. This may be dangerous since it can create mental passivity in the one being ministered to and can make them even more vulnerable to the possibility of falling over in a trance state. Whether people are pushed over or whether they fall, any deliberate attempt to imitate the activity of the Holy Spirit will only increase the likelihood of some form of humanly induced trance state in the emotionally vulnerable. Usually the only detrimental consequences are the embarrassment of falling over, and the disappointment if what was prayed for does not turn out as expected. Occasionally if there is idolatry present (some focusing on someone or something other than God), then dangerous counterfeit experiences may occur which will cause trouble for those involved.

Gassner continued to conduct his healing meetings for

about fifteen years and thousands flocked to be delivered of their ills. Others came just to watch what went on and among the crowds there were Protestant and Catholic, nobility and commoner. Support for his work came from some of his fellow Catholics but also from some notable Calvinist ministers of the day. Despite this support and the fact that Gassner invoked the name of Jesus in all his exorcisms, the official party line of the Catholic church was rather hesitant and eventually exorcism was banned altogether, firstly by the local archbishop of Salzburg and then by the Pope himself. After losing support from the ecclesiastical authorities of his time, Gassner's ideas and methods were then picked apart by the Bavarian Academy of Sciences. One of the scholars involved in the Academy's investigation was the now famous Franz Anton Mesmer. Mesmer went on to reinterpret what he saw at Gassner's meetings in terms of Animal Magnetism.

Franz Mesmer

Inspired by the spiritualist philosophy of Paracelsus, it was Franz Mesmer who, in the 1780s began to experiment with the idea of healing people through the induction of some form of trance. When he was expelled from his native Vienna for his unacceptable techniques, he sought refuge and opportunity in Paris. Here Mesmer flourished as he fascinated wealthy Parisians with his flamboyance and his healing power. He is remembered most for what became known as the 'baquet'. This was a large round oak tub that was filled with water, iron filings, magnets and even bits of broken glass (see Photo on page 92).

The 'baquet' was set in a large extravagantly decorated room and from its wooden lid protruded several loops of chain or metal handles. The patients were shown into the room and asked to sit down around the baquet and hold on to a piece of chain or a metal handle. Soft music began to play until, at a suitable moment, Mesmer would make a

This picture shows the centre-piece of Mesmer's method of trance induction. It was called the 'Baquet' and consisted of a large round oak tub. The tub was usually filled with water, iron filings, pieces of broken glass and magnets and had metal hoops or chains protruding from the top.

dramatic entrance dressed in expensive and flowing robes. As he strolled about the room he would arrestingly point at one of the gathering with his finger or his metal wand. It was not uncommon for that person to then fall to the ground with his or her limbs jerking in convulsions. Twitching, eyeball-rolling, strange grunts and cries, and hysterical laughter were also fairly common. The curious fact was that when these folk awoke from the ensuing coma (which almost always followed the convulsions), they often claimed to have been healed of their particular complaint.

In those days this sort of therapy was called 'Mesmerism' or 'Animal Magnetism'. Mesmer thought at first that a magnetic force from space, mediated by the planets and which emanated from the end of his wand or finger, was responsible for the cures and the unusual phenomena that he induced with his techniques.

Although Mesmer's techniques were more akin to showmanship, the results he produced were unquestionable. Cures were often reported, and so Louis XVI commissioned a group of scientists to subject his methods to examination. For some reason Mesmer himself decided to play truant during this scrutiny, preferring to leave matters in the capable hands of those who aided him in his mushrooming practice. This was probably a good thing, because Mesmer's flamboyant style may well have caused such offence, that a study of the actual method would have been overshadowed by emotional opinions about Mesmer himself.

Amid a flurry of publicity the investigating committee reported that his treatment consisted of a combination of the laying on of hands, 'stroking' and magnetism. One investigator, Jussieu, noticed that the magnetiser could influence a patient by an unseen gesture, and therefore there could be no doubt that there was some unexplained force 'which was exercised by man on man'. Despite this, the committee concluded by completely rejecting Mesmer's theory of animal magnetism, saying that the

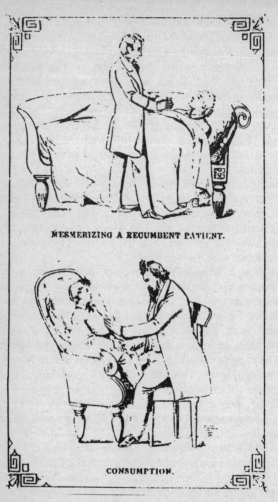

MESMERIZING A RECUMBENT PATIENT.

CONSUMPTION.

These engravings show how the Victorian hypnotherapist viewed his work. Both these pictures reveal how people believed that the healing power of the hypnotherapist emanated from the hands. Other pictures from the same period illustrate how the power to mesmerise (or hypnotise) was also thought to be the result of some

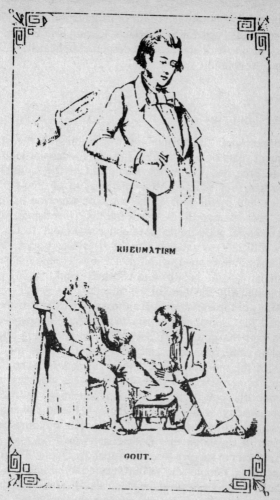

RHEUMATISM

GOUT.

*spiritual or occult force radiating from the hands of the mesmerist.
This image of mesmerism was propogated by books such as* Trilby
*by George du Maurier in which the wicked Svengali was depicted
as using similar mesmeric techniques to draw the innocent herione
'Trilby' into his power.*

healings were purely the result of imagination. So in 1784 Mesmer left Paris for Switzerland, leaving his disciples to carry on his work and face the desperate upheavals of the French revolution.

New Theories

Even through the turmoil of revolution and the subsequent years of Napoleon's reign, the French mesmerists made progress. Under the leadership of the Count de Puységur they adapted Mesmer's ideas to suit the public mood, and by the time of the battle of Waterloo in 1815 (the year Mesmer died), it was felt that convulsions were not essential or desirable for effective treatment. Instead it was sufficient to cause a sort of sleep-like trance state (somnambulistic state) within which it was found that suggestions about health and healing could easily be implanted into the mind of the subject.

Many of these nineteenth century mesmerists also abandoned the animal magnetism theories and adopted the idea that the power to induce a trance and bring about healing came from an occult force radiating from the fingers of the mesmerist (see Photos on pages 94 and 95). Though this new idea prevailed for a few decades, the mesmerists soon began to clean up their image because it was realised that mesmerism had uses in the area of anaesthesia. So they shed many of the occult trappings and jargon in the hope that mesmerism would be used for anaesthesia in surgery (see the Appendix Quote 'F'). But, quite often, people who were subjected to mesmerism for general surgery surprised the medical profession with their clairvoyant or 'second sight' gifts which manifested after the surgery. In one French faculty of medicine, a woman with no prior training amazed the medically qualified physicians by diagnosing the complaints of other patients in the ward, while she was still in trance.

*For James Braid and those trying to demystisize mesmerism the
main problem was the reality of the paranormal occurrences that
accompanied it. In this picture (circa 1838) a young French woman,
Leonide Pigeaire, is shown reading a book, line by line, despite
being blindfold. Although Braid had support from a number of
notable academics, his so called scientific explanations for the trance
state phenomena were rather improbable. Even current medical
experts are forced to describe them as psychic and possibly occult.*

Braid

Another attempt to rationalise the procedure of mesmerism was carried out by a Scottish surgeon, James Braid, in 1843. He wanted not only to dispel the occult associations of mesmerism, but also to divorce the phenomenon of trance states from witchcraft, with which it was usually linked. Since the old English word for inducing a trance was usually 'to fascinate' or 'to bewitch', Braid decided to coin a new and less occult sounding label for trance induction than these, or the rather tarnished one of 'mesmerism'.

Braid chose the word hypnotism from the Greek word 'hypnos' meaning sleep and he also devised a plausible theory about how trance induction worked. Braid suggested that the trance state was simply a neurological response to some form of physical distraction such as getting the subject to gaze at a bright object. But, as in France, Braid's subjects also tended to display psychic powers while in hypnotic trance. For instance, patients sometimes responded to gestures from the hypnotist which they could not see and some patients in trance could describe objects that were hidden from view. Like others before him, Braid attempted to cover up these occult manifestations with a semi-plausible cloak of scientific jargon.

Photo opposite
This engraving illustrates how surgery was performed around the time of Robert Lister (circa. 1870). Since the surgeons of the day were unsure of the principles of aseptic technique they still did not use sterile gloves, but worked with their bare hands amid a fine mist of carbolic. The anaesthetist is standing at the head of the patient who is being kept asleep with ether or chloroform. It was probably the timely discovery of these methods of anaesthesia which prevented hypnosis from being used more widely as a way of minimizing pain during surgery.

Braid was supported by three colleagues. Notably, W.B. Carpenter, Professor of Physiology at the University of London, sided with Braid on the aspect of the theory of hypnotism by agreeing that the mesmeric trance was a neurological phenomenon. He also helped Braid in his attempt at proving that the accompanying psychic/occult phenomena (i.e. convulsions, telepathy, second sight and clairvoyance), were not occult but the result of physiological changes as yet undiscovered.

Other supporters were Dr John Elliotson in England and Dr James Esdaile in India. Esdaile proved the practical usefulness of hypnotism by performing painless surgical operations using what was known as 'mesmeric anaesthesia'. In France hypnosis had also been used successfully in surgery and Dr J.E. Oudet had pioneered painless tooth extraction by inducing a 'magnetic sleep' in his patients. These unquestionable successes gave the subject of hypnotism some considerable impetus, until in 1846 William Morton of the United States proved that ether could be successfully employed as an anaesthetic agent in surgery (see Photo on page 99).

This discovery was quickly taken up by surgeons in Britain – notably Robert Lister – and soon became widely used, relieving doctors and surgeons of the need to learn a practice about which they felt most uneasy. This uneasiness of mesmerism/hypnotism had been fostered by the occasional appearance of unwelcome and unexplained psychic/occult phenomena, dubbed 'higher phenomena', which seemed to manifest while subjects were in hypnotic trance.

'Higher Phenomena'

One reason why some orthodox doctors decided to spurn hypnosis during the 19th century was probably their unwillingness to take on board something new. However the most off-putting aspect of the trance states was that hypnotised subjects quite often discovered paranormal abilities. The reasons put forward for these weird and often frightening occurrences were usually that hypnosis made people extraordinarily sensitive to the five senses of smell, touch, sight, sound and taste. But, when faced with inescapable proof of happenings that were totally divorced from the five senses, researchers had to concede that trance states must have connections with occult or spiritualist powers.

During some experiments hypnotised people could accurately judge the time even though they had no clock. This meant that a hypnotist could programme his subject to perform a particular task at a specific time without the person being aware of it. Other 'higher phenomena' included hallucinations, and researchers found that it was quite easy to suggest to a hypnotised person that someone or something was present when in fact this was not the case. One illustrious French researcher suggested to a subject in trance that in 63 days time he would go to his colleague's house and meet the President. Sure enough, 63 days later the man arrived on his colleague's doorstep and began to address him as the President of France, completely believing him to be his illustrious head of state.

Other paranormal trance state phenomena that were seriously investigated included telekinesis, dowsing and unnatural physical strength. (Telekinesis is the activity by which hypnotised people move objects, even quite heavy ones, without touching them.) Sometimes frail and slightly-built ladies astounded trance state researchers by lifting with ease those objects that even fit strong men would find difficult. Concerning dowsing, one investigator noticed that effective dowsers usually entered a trance state before they set off across a field to discover hidden springs of water or deposits of coal or metals.

Mediumistic Abilities

In addition to these phenomena, investigators confirmed that trance states could cause mediumistic abilities like

clairvoyance and second sight in which someone hypnotised could describe hidden articles, even things which
were placed some considerable distance away. But perhaps the most startling mediumistic trance state phenomenon was what was labelled 'dual or multiple
personalities'. In trance, it was commonly found that a few
subjects could take on the outward appearance of someone totally different. Their voice would sound different
and a new personality would take over and behave differently, often more intelligently than usual and sometimes rather sinisterly. The researchers of the day believed
that these changes in personality were simply different
expressions of the same person. Today's psychic
researchers would probably agree, but both seem to fail to
recognise the distinct similarities between dual or multiple
personalities in hypnotised people, and demonic possession in spiritualist mediums. Mediums who invoke the
power of what they believe are 'good' spirits during trance
often change their manner, memories, thought patterns
and tone of speech in a way that most psychologists would
identify as being an expression of a complementary personality. So without knowing it, researchers, both now
and in the past, could well have been inviting demon
possession in the subjects on whom they experimented.

Trances and Hysteria

During this era of research into trance state phenomena
the most useful of all was thought to be that of anaesthesia. However, it was not only possible to bring about
complete insensibility to pain by suggestion during hypnosis, but also sometimes to prevent the tissue damage
caused by painful injuries such as cuts and burns. With this
in mind Pierre Janet, a French researcher of the late 19th
century, discovered that he could cause tissue damage by
suggestion, and he managed to produce under hypnosis
what to all appearances was a real burn.

As scientists began to consider the implications of these

findings they began to re-examine the ecstatic experiences of mystics. St. Francis of Assisi, for instance, was reported to have experienced the phenomenon of the stigmata (the appearance of wounds on the body similar to those which Jesus received when he died for us on the cross). Instead of believing that it was an act of God, researchers redefined the stigmata as a trance state phenomenon brought on by the rigours of monastic life and intense meditation on the crucifixion. Later on, other ecstatic experiences began to be seen in this light and the Jesuit, H. Hahn speculated that the experiences of St. Teresa of Avila were a form of hysteria since she suffered from heart pains, nausea, nail biting, trances, paralysis and hallucinations. Certainly the bizarre nature of what happened to St. Teresa must make us question whether her experiences were inspired by God.

Directly associating hypnosis with convulsions, paralysis and the other physical symptoms of hysteria, a well known French neurologist called Charcot, began to postulate that the hypnotic trance was in fact some form of hysterical illness. Although this theory was not consistent with the accumulating weight of scientific evidence, it provided a suitable excuse for caution, and prevented the wholesale use of hypnosis in medicine during the first part of the 20th century.

Charcot

Jean-Martin Charcot, a neurologist from Paris, provided evidence in 1883 which seemed to prove that the hypnotic trance was a form of hysteria, in short a neurological disorder. He did this by mimicking the symptoms usually displayed in hysteria (i.e. loss of control of muscles leading to convulsions or paralysis), by inducing them in his hypnotised subjects. He concluded that the convulsions which sometimes accompanied hypnosis were due to hysterical muscular hyperexcitability, and the trance itself was a man-made form of epileptic fit.

Annoyed that the hypnotic trance was being presented as some sort of nervous illness, these conclusions were challenged by two French doctors, Liébeault and Bernheim, who were practising hypnotherapists from the Lorraine area of eastern France. They tried to defend hypnosis by experimentally demonstrating that the hypnotic trance was not just an induced state of hystero-epilepsy. Although successful, they also confirmed the suspicion that hypnotism liberated unwanted psychic forces, telepathy and clairvoyance etc. For example, in the concurrent investigations carried out by Pierre Janet, it was found that a hypnotist could influence someone who had already been hypnotised at a distance of half a mile away. It was also discovered that a person could be hypnotised without being aware of it, sometimes at a considerable distance from the hypnotist. These examples definitely disproved Charcot's theory and were said to be examples of telepathy or thought transference which some believed was the result of hypersensitive hearing abilities!

Although a British enquiry into the work of these early French hypnotherapists proved very favourable, public opinion in Britain remained convinced of the occult involvement in hypnosis. So the subject was quietly swept under the carpet as the breakthroughs of Pasteur, Koch and others held the medical limelight during the last decade of the nineteenth century.

Freud

Other illustrious men took an interest in the trailblazing work of Liébeault and Bernheim, notably Sigmund Freud.

Freud first heard of these Frenchmen through Charcot, to whom he had gone in 1885, so that he could learn more about the neurological (nervous) processes of the body. Charcot not only exposed Freud to some new theories about hysteria, but also kindled within him an irresistible desire to find out more concerning hypnotism. So in 1889 Freud returned to France from Vienna, this time as the pupil of Bernheim, intent on discovering as much as possible about the then fashionable phenomenon of hypnosis. Impressed by what he saw and learnt, he returned home with the express intention of perfecting the use of hypnosis in recalling forgotten trauma, so that appropriate emotions, previously repressed, could be released. For a while he worked alongside another Viennese doctor with some experience of hypnosis, Dr Josef Breuer, but becoming disenchanted with hypnotic techniques, Freud decided to branch off and begin his investigations into what has now become known as psychoanalysis.

Some present-day hypnotherapists think that Freud abandoned hypnosis because he could not induce a deep enough trance to carry out sufficiently effective therapy in every patient that he treated. Freud himself gives other reasons.

Freud declared that the results he achieved with hypnotised patients were only temporary and rather unpredictable. He called hypnosis 'his temperamental and, one might almost say, mystical ally' and disapproved of the ethics of suggestive therapy with its 'deceit, coercion and ignorance.' Although Freud generally ignored the occult side-effects of hypnosis, such as telepathy, he was disturbed by them and recalls in his writings the amusing but frightening incident when, after waking a female patient from trance, he found himself forcibly embraced. He records being saved by the unexpected entrance of his servant but from that time on he remained suspicious about the unpredictable side-effects of hypnosis which sometimes occurred.

However Freud's main objection to hypnosis was its tendency to gloss over problems in the mind. He felt that using hypnotic trance and the prohibitory suggestion (where the hypnotist suggests that any symptoms of illness will disappear) tended to cover up the real problem, and therefore make it more inaccessible to proper treatment.

Later on in life Freud further commented on the hypnotic trance. While he recognised that it often saved much time, 'monotonous' was the word which he used to describe the continuous repetition of having to induce trance and then simply insert suggestions that the offending symptoms were gone. He said that this was not scientific activity, but reminded him of 'incantations of magic and other hocus pocus' (see the Appendix Quote 'J').

Hypnosis and Humanism

As the twentieth century dawned, few people imagined the horror of the wars that were to occur within its first fifty years. But it was the trauma experienced by soldier and civilian alike that was to further the cause of hypnosis. Men who suffered in the trenches and those whose lives had been devastated by the ravages of war, began to appear at the psychologist's door expecting help for their hurts.

It seems also that the psychologists themselves had been affected since these global tragedies had twisted their thinking to exclude the existence of a caring all-powerful God. The seeds of error sown by the theory of evolution back in the 1850s, had given medical people the confidence to assert that the concept of a God was simply 'a convenient crutch' for the weak. The strong believed that they had no need of God, and psychologists began to experiment with ways to help their fellow humans by every means except with reference to God. This, in a nutshell, is humanism.

Hypnosis fared well in this environment where any reference to a spiritual dimension could be conveniently ignored behind a smoke-screen of scientific jargon. But, as in the past, scientists were faced with the task of explaining away those awkward but constantly recurring occult/psychic side-effects of hypnosis. One of these was the phenomenon of 'past life experiences'. Damaged people who went for hypnosis were told that hypnosis could help them relive traumatic events in their lives and express the appropriate emotions which had, until then, been suppressed. This is called 'abreaction'. As well as reliving past experiences in their lives, people sometimes said that they had relived 'past lives' during hypnotic trance. Scripture is quite clear that a man or woman lives once only and then they either go to be with the Lord (Luke 23:43) or they go to some appointed place to wait for judgement (Hebrews 9:27). Therefore the accounts of past life experiences, however plausible, must be either a made-up story or a demonic deception, probably the latter.

Automatic Writing

During the early part of this century, another phenomenon needing to be explained was the popular use of automatic writing during hypnotic trance.

In an experiment a hypnotised subject would be told a story or a word and then he would be brought out of trance and asked whether he remembered what was said to him in trance. If the answer was obviously 'no', the hypnotist would effectively blindfold the subject, give him a paper and pencil and ask him to write as he felt moved. The hand of the subject would mysteriously move across the paper and apparently describe the story or the word that was given during trance.

Anita Muhl, a foremost authority on automatic writing vigorously declared that it had nothing to do with the occult and, with other researchers, believed it to be the activity of the 'under self'. But their sometimes bizarre experimental results, and the fact that automatic writing is widely used among spiritualist mediums means that occult activity cannot be ruled out. Furthermore Dr Marcelo Augusto Cardoso, a Brazilian gynaecologist who studied psychic phenomena (parapsychology) for twenty years, declared after he became a Christian that parapsychological phenomena are manipulated by Satan. In his authoritative testimony he stated that 'levitation, materialisation and extra-sensory perception are not things which you exercise alone, but with the help of spirit beings'.

Another more recent trance state manifestation similar to that of automatic writing is what is called the 'hidden observer'. This phenomenon was first observed during some research work into the feasibility of using hypnosis as a way of removing pain during surgery.

Scientists often refer to the 'hidden observer' as a sub-conscious awareness (or personality) which is occurring at the same time as the conscious processes such as hearing or seeing. But the fact that the 'hidden observers' usually only express themselves through automatic writing, ouija boards and other psychic activities indicates that there may well be something more sinister beneath the surface.

The 'hidden observer' is encountered when one of the senses is blocked by hypnotic suggestion. For example, by suggestion a hypnotist may cause complete numbness in a subject's arm, and then plunge it into ice cold water. Since the hypnotised person verbally reports that they can feel no pain, the 'hidden observer' may be asked to recount what the body is really feeling, and through automatic writing is said to do so with some degree of accuracy. Other senses may also be affected by hypnotic suggestion. Sight and hearing for instance, can be blocked and, even though the hypnotised subject denies seeing or hearing anything, the 'hidden observer' is said to report the sights and sounds to which the subject is exposed.

Because of the humanist basis for most scientific work into these paranormal effects, researchers usually exclude the occult and develop some theory about the subconscious to explain them. This means that they often deceive themselves and others. In spite of their intellectual brilliance, they will not believe the Bible which positively affirms the existence not only of a loving, caring God, but also of a host of opposing spiritual forces intent on harming and ultimately destroying God's creation, particularly men and women.

The phenomena of past life experiences and the 'hidden observer', hint that even in the clinical, supposedly rational, environment of modern day medical research, occult things may occur but be ignored or attributed to man's unfathomable subconscious mind.

What Does History Teach Us?

Throughout this fairly brief look at the history of hypnosis, two important facts seem to be repeated. Firstly, a hypnotic trance can be induced for healing purposes in a variety of ways. Greatraks used his techniques of stroking, Mesmer brought about therapeutic trance states by simply pointing at someone with a wand (or just his finger), and Braid hypnotised his subjects by getting them to stare at a pinpoint of light. Furthermore, counterfeit Christian healing involving trance states can be brought about by the ritual of touching some venerated relic or by visiting a sacred shrine.

The second and most important fact which we can learn from history, is that humanly induced trance states may well invite the activity of unseen evil spiritual forces. This occult involvement in hypnosis is clearly displayed by the occurrence of trance state phenomena such as multiple personalities, telekinesis, telepathy and clairvoyance. Whenever hypnosis or trance states have been used to bring healing, even in the clinical environment of a research laboratory, occult or paranormal happenings seem to take place.

Ever since the middle of the 19th Century, scientists have attempted to rationalise these extraordinary events with rather unlikely pseudo-scientific explanations. Rational thinking, however, does not satisfy the spiritual vacuum in men and women, and so 'New Age' theories have been embraced which openly admit the spiritual dimension but which strongly deny that Jesus Christ is the only answer to man's spiritual needs. 'New Age' thinking leads people to accept all paranormal events without questioning where they came from. Those who start by dabbling in hypnosis may well end up openly (but unknowingly) interacting with evil forces who are only intent on debasing and destroying human life as God created it.

Chapter 7

Other Therapies Involving Hypnosis

Self-Hypnosis

'There is nothing new under the sun,' declared the preacher in Ecclesiastes (Ecclesiastes 1:9), and this is well borne out in the arena of hypnosis. Many think of self-hypnosis as something quite novel, but in reality it has been practised by Buddhist monks, Hindu fakirs, witchdoctors and soothsayers throughout history. The object of these self-induced trance states has almost always been of an occult, supernatural nature. The most extreme feat involving self-hypnosis is performed by yogis, fakirs and voodoo priests, and involves the reduction of bodily activity, including the heart, by the induction of a very deep trance state. As proof of their apparent ability to control the spiritual forces of evil they have themselves put away in coffins or incarcerated in stone vaults for periods of between three and ten weeks with a pre-arranged agreement for someone to come and wake them when the time has expired.

Self-hypnosis is also used by firewalkers in the Hindu, Buddhist and animist religions. Those about to walk on hot coals send themselves into a deep hypnotic state by fasting, meditation and by continuously repeating certain 'mantras'. Again these 'coal strollers' are trying to display their spiritual potency, and the trance state is their way of making contact with the spiritual forces whom they hope will protect them.

Today, self-hypnosis (or autohypnosis) is becoming popular in Western society to enable, as the famous hypnotherapist Milne Bramwell once stated, the patient to 'gain increased control over his own organism.' Some of the physical disorders said to be helped by self-hypnosis are angina (pectoris), palpitations, headaches, stomach/intestinal disorders, insomnia, obesity and localised pain. Also a very common use of self-hypnosis is when some effect is required at a later date. Perhaps someone, who hates needles, wants to be calm and pain free during his or her visit to the dentist, or an expectant mum wishes to be relaxed and pain free when her baby is delivered. Self-hypnosis is becoming widely used in this sort of context.

It works like this. The hypnotist teaches clients how to hypnotise themselves, usually by encouraging them to 'relax and let their mind drift until their attention is shifted to inside their own head.' Once this has been learned, and the subjects have become quite experienced at inducing a state of trance, the hypnotist will then show them how to give themselves therapeutic suggestions.

Directed Daydreaming

Another scenario in which hypnosis and self-hypnosis is gaining popularity is in the treatment of certain irritating skin diseases. Sufferers, more particularly children, are taught how to induce a state of hypnosis by staring at a coin and repeating phrases that suggest they are going to relax. Once in a state of trance they then begin to develop a fantasy that has been previously suggested by their doctor or hypnotist. This fantasy is carefully designed to make them less aware of their itching skin. For instance, if the skin complaint has the characteristic of being hot, the prearranged fantasy will involve a beautiful snow-covered landscape where the patient is taught to imagine the feeling of cool snow on his or her skin. This form of hypnosis has been skilfully dubbed 'guided fantasy' or 'directed daydreaming', so that negative ideas and fears about the term hypnosis (and its less pleasant background/ associations/history) are not allowed to undermine the therapy for the children or their parents.

Doctors who teach people these techniques warn that it is best to learn them from a trained therapist because a small percentage of the population is very vulnerable to self-hypnosis. The danger is that someone will choose the wrong trance induction cues and therefore may inadvertently hypnotise themselves at some inappropriate moment.

Self-Improvement

Techniques of self-hypnosis are often used by people who are keen to improve themselves or their performance at work, in the family or elsewhere. While self-improvement is often encouraged in the Bible, it is always promoted in the context of a dependent relationship with Jesus. The Bible says *'be holy'* and *'love one another'* but all these commands are given on the understanding that *'without me you can do nothing'* (John 15:5). The following example is a personal testimony of a woman who used hypnosis as a source of enjoyment, saying it helped to integrate her personality.

Case History HYP/M (see Bibliography No. 32)

... 'I decided to use hypnosis to prompt my unconscious mind to give me direct communication in the form of dreams. That is to say, I put myself into a dream-like state which I called a hypnotic dream.

'The first dream I had was reassuring. I dreamed I saw a message written on the wall in chalk which promised me, "Dreams will help you and you will achieve satori" (see footnote). (I was very surprised to read the word "satori"

Footnote
Satori is a state of intuitive illumination (or sudden state of knowledge or ability gained without effort) sought in Zen Buddhism.

because I scarcely know what it means.) I was delighted with this message, because it showed me I was on the right track, had the co-operation of my whole mind, and felt I was right to trust my unconscious mind. Since then I have had other dreams and met helpful characters who have promised to help me in my dreams and in my waking life. I have met a medicine man to help me to keep my health and a kind and gentle woman to help me express my negative emotions'...

This fearful example shows how people are being deluded into thinking that hypnosis is purely a psychological phenomenon. This unfortunate, perhaps lonely, woman has, through self-hypnosis, opened herself up to evil spirits that are posing as characters within her mind who want to help her. I have no doubt that their influence will eventually cause her health to deteriorate rather than improve. I am sure that a supportive church with understanding, gentle and Holy Spirit filled ladies would have been a better place for her to work out those negative emotions which, like many of us, she was finding so difficult to handle.

Autogenic Training

Hypnotherapists have adopted many of the occult practices of the East, refining them to suit their purposes. Techniques such as autosuggestion, autogenic training and some relaxation methods are simply forms of yoga or occult meditation (i.e. meditation involving idolatry or worship of foreign gods) with a whitewash of scientific jargon over them (see the Appendix Quote 'L').

Autogenic training was first devised in 1959 by Schultz and Luthe as a series of simple exercises involving autosuggestion for the purpose of inducing a therapeutic hypnotic trance. The exercises start by concentrating on a particular limb, with the participant continuously repeating a phrase like, 'my right arm is becoming heavy', or 'my right arm is becoming warm'. Progressively, more advanced autosuggestive exercises follow in which the overall aim is to gain greater control over the body's involuntary functions (i.e. bowels, heart, etc.) by suggesting changes during trance.

Once the participant has learnt the first stage of trance induction by autosuggestion two further programmes follow. These are:

1. Single focus concentration as practised in Yogic meditation. For example, staring at the end of one's nose.
2. Meditation on the abstract qualities of the universe, much as in Yogic or Zen meditation (see the Appendix Quote 'M').

Usually only the first programme is used to complement the introductory exercises in the therapeutic treatment of certain disorders, like anxiety, insomnia and mild hypertension. However even the preliminary exercises are said to be enough to induce extremely deep trance states, deep enough even to bring about experiences of a mystical nature. Some autogenic trainees have described that they temporarily lost their sense of personal identity and felt a sort of mystical union with nature, others have reported levitation and experiences which are common in oriental types of meditation.

As with Transcendental Meditation, Yoga and Zen Buddhism, these techniques directly employ some form of hypnotic trance to achieve goals that could be more safely addressed if they were related to Jesus Christ. Jesus said,

> 'come unto me, all you who labour and are heavy laden and I will give you rest. Take my yoke upon you and learn of me, for I am meek and lowly in heart: and you shall find rest for your souls. For my yoke is easy and my burden is light.' (Matthew 11:28–30)

These are not just comfortable words, they are a comfortable reality to those who rely upon and trust in the Lord during their daily experience. We do not need to be sidetracked by these Hindu/Buddhist based, idolatrous techniques for relaxation, as they most certainly will not bring true rest to our souls.

Autosuggestion (Couéism)

Finally, in the family of self-help therapies directly based on hypnotism, we need to consider the practice of autosuggestion. This form of therapy is similar in principle to 'positive thinking' but is very frequently used in conjunction with a self-induced hypnotic trance.

Although 'positive thinking' has been known about and applied for centuries, the term autosuggestion was first coined by a Frenchman, Emile Coué. He was a pupil of Liébeault and Bernheim of the Nancy School of Hypnotherapy, but he also owned an apothecary business in his home town. Sometimes Coué claimed that sick people bought medicine from him and got better despite the fact that the medicine had no known beneficial effects. Others he noted, worsened despite taking proven remedies, and this forced him to conclude that the attitude of the patient was all important. In 1920 he introduced his own form of psychotherapy that was based on the prior induction of a light trance or a relaxed mood, and involved the endless repetition of a particular verbal formula which went like this, 'Every day, in every way, I am becoming better and better.' This mantra-like formula was to be repeated in a dull monotonous voice emphasising 'in every way' in order to remind the imagination that the aim was not just to remove any offending symptoms, but also to activate the 'life force' to promote better health in general. Coué's philosophy and his formula (called Couéism) became extremely fashionable in the French upper classes and spread rapidly within western high society. Through his methods Coué believed that he taught others to heal themselves and therefore is seen by some as the father of the present-day fad of 'self-help healing'.

Autosuggestion
Modern techniques of autosuggestion involve the playing of pre-recorded messages which are sometimes set to dreamy music.

Coué claimed that many organic changes within the body could be affected by his brand of autosuggestion. Though I do not doubt this, most forms of self-help therapy only serve to increase a person's independence of God, and therefore decrease the likelihood that he or she will come to a saving knowledge of the Lord Jesus. The prior induction of an hypnotic trance will also probably only aggravate this condition, since trance states can open up the mind of a man or a woman to the activities of evil spirit beings.

People are introduced to techniques of autosuggestion through listening to pre-recorded tapes that seek to help with particular problems. For those with low self-esteem there are tapes which encourage listeners to repeat out loud positive statements about themselves. Usually included on these tapes are portions of dreamy music which, accompanied by a relaxation script, are designed to induce a trance state. Sometimes the dreamy music is interwoven with subliminal messages (see footnote) that are put in for the benefit of listeners without them knowing it.

Christian Science

Although Coué formalised the practice of autosuggestion in the early part of the 20th Century, the idea that the mind could be mobilised to bring healing to the body was not new. One 'mind over matter' philosophy which became quite popular at the end of the 19th Century was a distortion of the true gospel of Jesus Christ known as Christian Science.

This erroneous pseudo-Christian teaching took root when Mary Patterson, who was a chronic invalid, went to Phineas Quimby of Maine, USA, for treatment in 1862. Phineas Quimby was a drugless healer and he used a number of rather odd rituals to transfer illness from the patient to himself, by what he believed to be electrical activity. He explained that once he had received an illness he would destroy it by the power of his mind. In fact, his ideas were probably based upon animal magnetism or hypnotism which had been readily imported from Europe since the time of Mesmer. Quimby believed that all illness was attributable to factors in the mind, and therefore

---

Footnote

Subliminal messages, whether heard or seen, are understandable messages that have their effects below the level of conscious awareness. Put more simply they are neither consciously seen or heard, and yet they are able to influence our behaviour. Subliminal messages on television are communicated by interrupting the normal flow of pictures for a fraction of a second. The message is exposed for such a short period of time that it does not register consciously. Research, however has conclusively proved that these messages can have a profound effect. On radio or tapes subliminal messages are dubbed over the main sound using frequencies that are not consciously audible. In the USA any subliminal messages must, by law, be printed in block capitals on the sleeve of the tape or on the TV screen for a prescribed period of time.

Quimby began to develop the idea of do-it-yourself treatment by self-hypnosis (using autosuggestion).

Mary Patterson, who later became Mary Baker Eddy, was ripe ground for this form of self-help philosophy, since she had already formulated the theory that 'all disease is in the mind'. From this she deduced that 'as disease is what follows the error (in the mind or thinking), destroy the cause and the effect will cease.' Mary Patterson found that destroying the cause was a problem until, of course, she visited Quimby. She was herself cured of her own problem (only temporarily) and from then on began to develop her theories of self-help healing based on some of Quimby's ideas.

In 1875, after another experience of healing and subsequent spiritual illumination, she presented her book *Science and Health*. In it she contended that disease is an illusion and that it can only exist in the person who believes it exists. The cure for those already ill could be summed up in her own words:

> 'If you fill your mind with thoughts of self-confidence, courage, outward activity and interest in the glowing and vital things of life, then morbid ideas will be turned out of doors and there will be no vacant spot to which they can return.'

Mrs Eddy, as she now was, also claimed that *Science and Health* had been given to her by direct divine, verbal inspiration. In spite of this she went on to revise her original manuscript many times. In her writings she also encouraged her readers to study the Bible, using her book as the key to the Scriptures.

In reality her book, from the first to the last edition, is no more than a mass of confused ideas which are often repeated with some accompanying contradictions. What seems to attract readers is that the book contains statements which sound quite profound and which espouse the belief that healing can be achieved using the power of the mind.

Today some people still claim to find healing through Christian Science, but it is likely that self-hypnosis and autosuggestion are the reasons for its success. The attraction for Christians appears to be that Christian Scientists regularly refer to the sayings of Jesus, and do so in the context of his obvious compassion for the sick. The major deception in Christian Science lies in the fact that there is absolutely no teaching on the need for a personal salvation from sin. This means that Jesus is regarded merely as a good teacher and that his teachings simply instruct people in what they should, or should not do and believe, to find health.

Visualisation

Although not directly related to hypnosis there is one form of mental gymnastics that can invoke similar powers to those employed in self-hypnosis. This is visualisation or 'guided imagery'.

Visualisation is most commonly used by those people who have diseases that are not very successfully treated by conventional methods (e.g. cancer). After beginning with a ritual session of relaxation, people with diseases like cancer are told to picture their lungs or brain (or wherever they have problems) together with a dark menacing tumour. Then they are instructed to visualise the tumour decreasing in size until it is completely gone. Despite what any doctors tell them, subjects are encouraged to believe what they imagine, and use their mental powers to cure themselves.

These techniques which use the power of the imagination can be enhanced by hypnosis without the subject realising it. This is particularly true of the recent vogue of stress control tapes in which listeners are firstly invited to lie down somewhere quiet and relax. Then, beginning with the head and working downwards, they are told to firstly tense up and then relax the muscles of their body (a typical method of trance induction). After this they are asked to visualise themselves in a balloon. First of all the balloon is firmly fixed to the ground by many heavy loads of ballast. These, the listeners are told, are their worries and cares. These weights are progressively recognised and cut away and they begin to imagine themselves sailing away into idyllic countryside, everything below and behind them. When this imaginary balloon trip is over, the listeners are reassured that their problems are still under control, as they were when they imagined themselves far above them in the balloon.

Peaceful country scenes and faraway Pacific islands are the settings for other visualisation exercises. Sometimes the ritual cues for relaxation seem totally innocuous, but on other tapes they are more obviously hypnotic, like staring at a spot on the ceiling. So, under the guise of stress control and performance improvement, self-hypnosis has been subtly introduced into the lives of busy men and women.

Some Christians have suggested that this form of visualisation could be used within a biblical framework. Instead of cutting weights off a balloon, we could visualise all our worries as heavy hand luggage that needs to be handed over to Jesus. This would seem to be an appropriate way of visualising Peter's exhortation to *'cast all your cares upon him* (Jesus) *because he cares for you'* (1 Peter 5:7). It sounds good, especially for Christians who are easily anxious, but it may actually frustrate the power of the gospel in their lives.

For, when we try to combat the anxieties in our life, God does not want us to attempt to rationalise them with Scripture or even to pretend that we are not worried. This is the same as saying that we do not need God. Instead we need to trust Jesus to change us (see 1 John 1:9) so that we are at peace even in the most testing of circumstances. This way may take a little longer but it avoids the risk of self-hypnosis that is commonly tied up with visualisation and it also helps us to understand that God loves us just as we are, and not just when we think that we are getting it

all right. Perhaps it is fair to say that God is more interested in changing us from within rather than seeing us
develop complex coping mechanisms (even scripturally
based ones), which rely upon our own mental agility and
will-power for their success.

Inner Healing

Visualisation or a form of it, has also been used by some
Christians involved in caring for damaged or emotionally
disturbed people. Sometimes when people have suffered a
traumatic experience, Christian counsellors have guided
sufferers to imagine Jesus in the situation and allow him to
minister his love to them. Although there is a real danger
that this sort of therapy will become an exercise in manipulating the imagination of the sufferer, it may also provide
a genuine opportunity for the Holy Spirit to heal an area
of damage. This is because Jesus is, in reality, present in
every situation and he knows exactly what is going on in
the hearts and minds of those involved in some accident or
crime. Through his all-knowing presence he is able to
comfort, reassure, heal and reconcile the victim. He is
there also to heal, forgive and change the one who has
caused the harm.

When the woman caught red-handed in the act of adul-
tery was brought to Jesus (John chapter 8), he showed his
characteristic mercy and justice. Justice would be fulfilled,
Jesus knew, when he went to the cross. Therefore, he
could show mercy and say *'Where are your accusers* (those
who would have you put to death)? ... *neither do I con-
demn you ... Go and sin no more.'* No doubt, the woman
walked away from Jesus and the crowd assured of her
forgiveness. But, more than this, Jesus had lovingly made
her aware of the damage that her sin had caused. Perhaps
she went home and made up with her husband, who,
having seen the mercy of Jesus, was himself ready for
reconciliation. In this example from the New Testament
Jesus was actually present and therefore able to bring his

loving attitudes to bear on those involved. In Holy Spirit orientated inner healing, Jesus is present through the counsellors as they seek to represent his loving attitudes through the wisdom that has been given to them by God. Sometimes this wisdom will have been learnt through their experience of God's hand in their own lives. Other times they may feel inspired by the Holy Spirit to give counsel that is beyond their years and experience.

Therefore by understanding that Jesus was present during some traumatic event, those who have been severely abused can be helped to face some long-held resentment or some repressed emotion. In this way the damage caused by destructive circumstances can be resolved and healed as the counsellors remain open to what the Holy Spirit is saying in the situation. The job of the counsellors is not to manipulate the person's imagination but simply to shed light on past experiences by illustrating the way that Jesus felt during them.

This sort of prayer counselling differs from the majority of visualisation techniques, in that the sufferer is only encouraged to recall something that really did happen. When we realise that Jesus is present in every situation we can begin to come to him with the emotions we are feeling or have felt, without fear of rejection. As we bring our difficulties to the light healing can take place, both of the mind, with its memories and distorted thought patterns, and of the body which is sometimes diseased due to the emotional damage.

In complete contrast, visualisation techniques are solely concerned with fantasies that have little or no connection with reality. These techniques quite often also involve some form of turning in on oneself, some sort of dreamy and detached state of mind, which may be the same as an hypnotic state.

Chapter 8

Trance-like States in Other Therapies

Scientists around the world have often puzzled over some of the cures claimed by certain therapists. Sometimes they have put forward complicated and far-fetched theories to try and explain these cures scientifically, but usually without being very convincing. One theory that provides an explanation for a number of perplexing therapies is that of healing through trance or trance-like states.

That acupuncture, acupressure, reflexology and some aspects of massage, aromatherapy, chiropractic and osteopathy are reliant on the induction of a trance-like state (? alpha state) may seem ridiculous at first. But, as is explained in this chapter, doctors and researchers are becoming more aware that states of increased suggestibility (trance) can be induced by a variety of ritualistic activities. The fact that hypnosis is not associated with these therapies at the moment, means that patients/clients will be more vulnerable because they will be completely offguard.

Why trance states have down the centuries been known to cause healings and supernatural phenomena is a mystery, until it is realised that supernatural powers (spirit powers), may be at work when someone is in a trance or similar state. The intention of these spiritual forces is ultimately evil despite the fact that they may cause short-term relief for the person 'cured'. Any short-term gains in health usually only lead to a deepening alienation from the love of God as shown by Jesus Christ who is God's gift to the world.

Acupuncture

Sticking needles in the skin according to centuries-old tradition and effecting a cure for a multitude of diseases may appear rather far-fetched. However, despite all the inconsistencies, modern medical authorities are generally beginning to accept acupuncture even if they shun the spiritualist philosophy behind it.

Many doctors and researchers have ingeniously devised theories to explain how placing needles in completely unrelated areas of the body can somehow cause pain relief. Their theories, though, are totally inadequate because what is practised is not compatible with what is theorised. Because of this more complex explanations have to be thought up to get round these inconsistencies. Furthermore, traditional Chinese acupuncturists claim to do much more than relieve pain. Typhoid, dysentery, whooping cough, acne, diabetes, deafness, blindness and even leukaemia are included in the list of diseases which many acupuncturists believe that their therapy will alleviate or cure.

What seems to cast further doubt on these so-called scientific theories of acupuncture is that the effects of sticking sharp objects in places on the surface of the body are not consistent. For instance if you prick your finger on a rose thorn or step on a drawing pin you cannot expect healing from disease or the relief of pain, even if the puncture site lies directly over an appropriate acupuncture point. What is more, if an ordinary doctor tries to emulate the acupuncturist by sticking needles in the right places to relieve pain or bring healing, quite often nothing happens. The excuse for this inconsistency is that the doctor is not familiar with the philosophy behind acupuncture and therefore does not needle the correct spots. This philosophy, which comes out of China's spiritualist heritage, is neither scientifically reasonable nor does it agree with basic anatomical observation (e.g. acupuncture philosophy claims that all acupuncture points are joined together by invisible lines called 'meridians'. These, like the points themselves, are imaginary and have never been proved to exist.). What is even more irrational, from my viewpoint, is that acupuncturists sometimes needle specific points on the surface of the ear when treating disease or relieving pain in a totally unrelated part of the body. It is said that every part of the body is represented by a specific point on the ear. This sort of thinking is neither confirmed by our knowledge of anatomy nor is it backed up by experience. I have yet to meet someone who has been cured of poor eyesight while they were having their ears pierced for earrings (usually done over the 'eye' acupuncture point on the earlobe)!

Acupuncture diagnosis, the method which acupuncturists use to find out what is wrong with their patients, is also seriously flawed. The mainstay of acupuncture diagnosis is dependent on finding six different expressions of the radial pulses at both the right and left wrists (12 altogether). This is not just difficult but impossible, especially if the patient has lost an arm in an accident. Traditionally this has not caused the Chinese any problems since a near relative holding on to the patient can reveal the same body vibrations enabling an adequate diagnosis from their pulses. This can include a prediction of future disease and a summation of past problems as well as telling the therapist what is currently wrong. Perhaps, therefore, acupunctural pulse diagnosis is better described as pulse divination.

The real reason for the cures and pain relief effected by acupuncture is quite possibly nothing more than something akin to hypnosis. Although this may seem a little far-fetched, a large number of quite eminent scientists and medical researchers have put forward hypnosis (or something similar) as the most reasonable explanation for the results of acupuncture therapy whether it is pain relief or the treatment of disease. This is partly because the other

If acupuncture is more than a trance state therapy based on the power of suggestion, then why do we not see healings and pain relief from experiences such as treading on a nail or pricking one's finger on a needle or rose thorn? (NB: There are numerous acupuncture points on both the hands and the feet.)

main scientific explanations for acupuncture have serious inconsistencies, and partly because acupuncture therapy does have all the essential ingredients for trance induction. Professor Wall, one of the most eminent researchers in this field, while expressing doubt over his previous statements that acupuncture is simply hypnosis, recognises 'that social and psychological mechanisms play a dominant role'.

This idea that acupuncture works by the induction of some form of trance is also reinforced by a number of well informed Christians in the Far East, where acupuncture is prevalent. A research paper from Singapore Bible College hinted that acupuncture probably worked through a mechanism similar to hypnosis. In addition, a Malaysian Pastor (who is also a doctor of medicine) claimed that the Holy Spirit gave him this word about acupuncture:

'Acupuncture was conceived and nurtured by a people who have never known me. It induces a trance-like state in the individual and renders people vulnerable to varying degrees of oppression and brings me no glory.'

This not only implicates trance states in acupuncture and its related therapies like acupressure and reflexology, but it also reminds us that some folk may be adversely affected by them. Though we need to weigh all prophecy, this simple 'revelation' (see 1 Corinthians 14:6) stands up well to close scrutiny and adds yet further weight to the argument that therapies like acupuncture probably do involve some form of trance-like state. (For a more in-depth analysis of acupuncture, see the Bibliography, entry No. 35.)

Active Trance States

Though it may be hard to believe that trance states can be induced by simply placing one or two needles on the surface of the skin, it has even been shown that people can experience trance states while doing exercise. Those involved in some form of rhythmical activity like running or cycling have sometimes been able to be deeply hypnotised despite the fact that they are not physically relaxing.

An example of self-induced active trance states is the practice of Tai-Chi ch'uan. In this Taoist method of meditation specific postures and movements are performed in conjunction with exercises in controlled nasal breathing. Great therapeutic benefit is said to be derived from doing these carefully prescribed motions which are not so different from shadow boxing. Those who practise Tai-Chi ch'uan regularly believe that it can not only help people overcome sickness, anxiety and mental fatigue but also give some adherents supernatural strength.

Supernatural strength is also the goal of the meditational techniques associated with the martial arts, in particular, Aikido and Karate. Karate 'black belts' often try to increase their potency by going to cold and solitary places and surviving with no food and only rudimentary clothing. One champion of Karate, who later became a Christian, related how this sort of rigorous training is usually not enough, and the Karate enthusiast is drawn deeper into meditative practices. These methods of meditation involve mind emptying and the production of a passive mental state in which it is possible to experience the supernatural. Once he felt his conscious self being detached from his body during a high speed simultaneous combat with 8–10 opponents and he watched himself from above as he fought off his attackers. This detachment of soul from body is called Astral Projection and is a common experience of those in deep trance states. It therefore appears likely that martial art meditation involves some kind of self-induced trance state.

Aromatherapy

It may be surprising to see aromatherapy linked with hypnosis and trance state therapies. But aromatherapy's popularity at psychic fairs and exhibitions broaching on the paranormal, have caused me to question why the phenomenon of smell can be so easily linked with the arena of the human psyche.

If we examine the methods employed by primitive cultures to induce trance we find that most of the five senses

---

Photo opposite
In this scene an African witchdoctor is said to be hypnotising the woman who is kneeling in front of him (probably for health reasons). He is using all the five senses except perhaps taste to distract the woman's conscious mind and so induce a state of increased suggestibility. He is touching her arms (touch), he appears to be transfixing her gaze (sight), the drum beats monotonously behind him (sound), and his female assistant wafts the incense(?) around (smell).

N° 437. Scène de magnétisme en Afrique. D'après M. Adalbert de Beaumont.

can be used. Obvious examples are the rhythmical swaying of a dancer (sight) or the droning effect of drums (hearing) as practised by tribal healers in numerous animist cultures. Usually the induction of a trance in their clients was (and still is) necessary to allow the spirits, which they worshipped, to gain entrance and effect a cure. Although the sense of touch is less well known as an hypnotic trigger, there is ample evidence from history that 'stroking' is an effective method of trance induction. Finally there are the senses of smell and taste, and the sense of smell is well known as a trance induction aid.

In Bali, as in other animist cultures, the healer priests use music and burn incense to produce trance states. The smell, when combined with the effect of the music, is designed to induce a trance and once again allow the spirits to possess the worshipper and give them the things which they feel they need.

The effectiveness of the sense of smell in helping bring about trance states should not surprise us. Often the first and most potent introduction when we enter a stranger's house is not what we hear or see but commonly what we smell. British hospitals used to be renowned for their clinical and rather unpleasant smell. It was often strong enough to repel even patients who were in dire need. Recently some hospital wards have done research on the effect of pleasant smells on anxious patients waiting for surgery and found that they have a small but useful effect. As with most smells, pleasant or foul, their effect is usually only transient, lasting at most only a few minutes, by which time the smell receptors in the nose readjust or 'adapt'. This means that even if the odour remains it will not register strongly in the smell centres of the brain for very long unless the person takes a deep breath in through their nose.

Because our smell receptors have this adapting ability, the clinical effect of any smell used in aromatherapy is probably limited to a few minutes only. It is this short period of (sometimes profound) effect which makes it so useful in inducing a trance state. The fact that smelling salts have been used for centuries as a means of reviving women who have fainted indicates how strong this effect can be.

Aromatherapy and Therapeutic Trance

Psychiatrists in England have recently examined the use of aromatherapy for preventing fits in known epileptics. Patients are asked to choose an essential oil (or oils) which they like the smell of. Using these oils they have several massages and then, during a subsequent session of hypnosis, the suggestion of deep relaxation is linked with the smell of the oils. Then every time the client feels an epileptic attack coming on, he is told to sit down in a quiet place and smell the oil (or oils), inhaling deeply.

Despite the researchers' sincere enthusiasm to find a cure for this debilitating problem we should not veer away from truth as we understand it. It is important to remember that humanly induced trance states are dangerous in that they can expose us to spiritual interaction – almost always negative.

Perhaps aromatherapy's use as an hypnotic trigger explains why it figures so prominently at psychic fairs and the like. People who go to these events are often looking for something to satiate that spiritual appetite which we all have. They feel that aromatherapy massage sessions will help them relax and improve their potential as human beings, and heighten their spiritual awareness. When they begin to hanker after more than the relaxing and sensual effects of aromatherapy, self-hypnosis and Zen or Yogic meditation associated with aromatherapy are often suggested. Participants are led to believe that trance state experiences will help them to be more fulfilled and happier people.

Many who are drawn into these experiences have been disillusioned by a misrepresentation of the true message of the gospel of Christ where Christian peace and joy have

133

largely been discredited. To some it is merely a message of a kind of bondage, to others a simple message for the naive mind. For the one who is honestly searching for truth and goodness, there is still a real and powerful answer in Jesus Christ. The abundant life he offers is completely free but can only be ours as we give him everything we are and have. It is here that those who would search for God will find him, hopefully before they are harmed by deceptive trance state experiences.

Since the powers of darkness are often trying to hijack the good things that God has created and make them their own, two notes of caution need to be sounded. The first is that many pungent smells arise from gasses that in themselves are clinically useful. For instance, eucalyptus is pleasant smelling and is effective as a nasal decongestant. Its medicinal power is not in the smell itself but rather in the ability of the gas to inhibit the secretion of nasal mucus. Secondly pleasant smells in themselves are, I believe, not to be despised when planning the care of sick people. Proverbs, chapter 27 verse 9, teaches that oil and perfume make the heart glad. Also God made incense a part of the fabric of Hebrew worship as an expression of the 'set-apartness' (holiness) of the worship of God's people, Israel. So our faculties of smell should, with our other senses, be set apart for God and enjoyed. This means that we ought to use smell to enhance life and bring glory to God. I believe that it is appropriate to alleviate the suffering of illness with sweet perfumes, but inappropriate to use them to induce an altered state of consciousness (i.e. a trance).

It is worth remembering that the massage aspect of aromatherapy can be used inappropriately as well. Usually massage is used to relax and loosen tense and sometimes painful muscles. Massage is said to increase the flow of blood to a muscle and encourage the flushing away of harmful chemicals deposited in it by strain or overactivity. Aromatherapists often incorporate massage in their

Aromatherapy Arm Massage

Although arm massage may seem totally innocuous, it is worth remembering that the gentle repetitive stroking of the forearm is a tried and tested method of trance induction. In the 1840s Dr James Esdaile of the East India Company used it to induce trance in patients about to undergo painful surgical procedures.

treatments so as to relax their clients and sometimes to help them enter trance states. Massage can also provide an opportunity for therapists to practise their psychic healing techniques. These appear rather similar to the 'laying on of hands' as outlined in the Bible (see Mark 16:18) but in reality the two procedures are totally opposite. Psychic healing is a self-centred spiritualist activity, but when believers lay hands on someone in obedience to God's command, then the result is wholesome, even if we do not always understand it.

Chiropractic and Osteopathy

Asthma, eczema, high blood pressure, heart failure, diabetes, and stomach ulcers; along with common backache, are the sort of illnesses claimed to be treatable by the alternative therapies, osteopathy and chiropractic. Although these therapies employ little more than minute but sudden movement of the joints that connect the bones of the spine (manipulation), many complicated and seemingly plausible theories have been devised which seek to justify such claims. But are these so-called scientific theories the real reason for the cures effected by chiropractic and osteopathy?

Historical Background

Although any connection between the two therapies is strongly resisted by each group, curiously both chiropractic and osteopathy started up in small towns in the USA that are situated not more than 150 miles apart. What makes some form of 'idea stealing' more likely is that the originators of these therapies shared a common interest in spiritualism and would meet up at spiritualist conventions. Furthermore they both began propagating their new ideas around about the same time.

Osteopathy was first off the starting blocks when in 1874 a man called A.T. Still set up shop as a local healer in Kirksville, Missouri. Though he was well versed in the anatomy of the body, and though he never overtly claimed to be a spiritualist, his philosophical leanings and his belief in psychic power seem to indicate that osteopathy, at the outset, was probably not based on an understanding of natural bodily processes. A.T. Still, though, was firmly convinced his new therapy was based on scientific principles which medically trained people had overlooked. However, in the light of what doctors know today, osteopathic ideas are becoming increasingly difficult to prove. A.T. Still's reliance on unscientific principles and powers is illustrated by the fact that he claimed to have healed by osteopathic manipulation such illnesses as measles, diphtheria, eczema, pneumonia, tuberculosis, mumps and gallstones to name but a few. He went on to

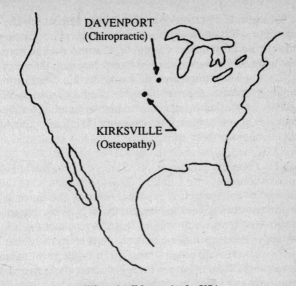

Where it all began in the USA
Between the years of 1874 and 1895 Osteopathy started up in Kirksville, Missouri and Chiropractic began in Davenport, Iowa. 150 miles separates these two towns.

say that his manipulative skills could treat almost any illness of mankind.

A.T. Still openly displayed his psychic powers not only by his ability to foresee future events, but also because he believed that the mind could be trained to see beneath the skin in the same way that X-rays do and this, perhaps, explains why he was often able to make rapid and accurate diagnoses. The fact that osteopaths today rarely attempt to emulate the healing feats of A.T. Still indicates that he was probably operating through psychic or occult powers.

Chiropractic came into being about 21 years later when D.D. Palmer claimed to have quite independently discovered 'the single cause of all disease'. Openly spiritualist and a dabbler in phrenology and magnetic healing (hypnosis), Palmer devised the theory that all disease is caused by 'subluxations' of the bones of the spine. These subluxations, he believed, were some sort of spinal deformity which caused illness because the vertebrae somehow were impinging on nearby nerves and interfering with the essential flow of nerve messages to the body. He went on to explain that these blockages in nerve conduction, impeded the flow of 'innate intelligence' which affected the functioning of all the organs of the body. D.D. Palmer thought that the cure for these spinal deformities was some kind of specialist manipulation of the spinal vertebrae.

D.D. Palmer's ideas and his concept of 'innate' have much in common with Chinese Taoist philosophy and the concept of 'ch'i', which is the label given to the universal life force said to govern human health. It is likely that this influence of Chinese mysticism was the result of his contact with Chinese coolies who were settling in the American Pacific ports like San Francisco in order to work on the railways. Palmer's son, who aggressively took over and some believed killed his father in a car accident, was an ardent Buddhist whose home became a sort of Buddhist paradise. Chiropractic's Taoist/Buddhist background indicates to me that, like acupuncture, it is a trance state therapy rooted in spiritism. Although it is more difficult to trace any direct Taoist influence in osteopathy, there are distinct similarities between what Palmer said (and even the way he said it) about 'innate' and the philosophy behind osteopathy which A.T. Still espoused.

Fact or Fiction?

Although osteopathy often stresses the importance of an unimpeded supply of blood to parts of the body, both osteopathy and chiropractic state that uninterrupted spinal nerve pathways are essential to good health. They would both say also that manipulation of the bones of the spinal column is the way to ensure that a nerve is freed from any constricting effects of the surrounding structures (what chiropractors called 'subluxations'). These subluxations, called 'osteopathic lesions' by osteopaths, are not visible on X-ray and are quite often diagnosed in different places by different therapists. This causes both osteopaths and chiropractors to claim that subluxations are 'dynamic' problems (that their presence is only seen when the patient moves) rather than being a bone or joint that is 'out of place'.

As with nearly all chiropractic and osteopathic theory it all sounds quite plausible, but closer examination reveals that subluxations could well be a figment of the chiropractor's or osteopath's imagination. More importantly, most relevant research on the subject indicates that those back problems, where nerves have definitely become trapped or pinched, very often cause little more than discomfort and some measure of immobility. To say, as chiropractic and osteopathic theory insists, that people become ill due to trapped spinal nerves is, to say the least, lacking in reliable scientific support. Furthermore the theories which attempt to explain how manipulation can cure these diseases do not conform to current knowledge on the behaviour of the nervous system.

Today physiotherapists and medical specialists in conditions of the muscles, nerves and bones are all aware that manipulation can, at least temporarily, relieve and mobilise stiff and painful joints. In some cases pain in an arm or leg can be traced back to a tense and tender area in the back which when treated with manipulation and/or gentle mobilisation also eases the limb discomfort. Therefore manipulation does have a place as a worthwhile, albeit limited, medical procedure. Some osteopaths and chiropractors, who are well informed and experienced at dealing with musculoskeletal problems, recognise the limitations and attempt to stay within their confines. Others, often similarly skilled, base their practice on the pseudo-scientific theories of their particular therapy. Despite good intentions I believe that these therapists are not only deceiving the folk who come to them for treatment but are also participating in activities which probably have spiritualist origins. As in the case of A.T. Still, some therapists may be using and developing psychic powers to treat their clients. These powers may appear harmless especially when they are presented within the context of a seemingly scientific framework. Osteopathic and chiropractic theories have sufficient physiological feasibility to satisfy casual observers or potential clients, but even in the light of current medical knowledge are highly improbable.

Trance-like States?

Perhaps another reason why some of these alternative therapists get unusual results is that they are using the power of suggestion and subtly induced trance-like states. Patients are convinced of the possibility of healing through the clever presentation of osteopathic or chiropractic theory. Then they wait expectantly for that inevitable, magical 'clicking' of their spinal vertebra (which in reality means nothing and in nearly every case does not prove that a vertebra has been forced back into its correct position). The healing, if it occurs, happens much in the same way that healing occurs during hypnosis where preconditioning, suggestion and a powerful element of distraction are the triad of events necessary for the effective induction of some form of trance state in the patient.

An interesting example of chiropractic treatment, where trance states may have been involved, occurred at the out-patients department of an English college of chiropractic during the 1980s. From all accounts, cases like this are fairly common and in this instance involved a boy of about 5 years of age, who for the previous two years had had quite severe episodes of asthma. The condition was so severe, that he was prescribed comparatively large doses of steroids to reduce the inflammation in the tubes of his lungs. The steroids were having some side-effects as well, so the boy's mother thought she would try chiropractic.

She was very impressed but noticed that after each treatment her boy was extremely relaxed and would sleep for hours. This was not normal for him but she was very satisfied since the boy's asthma improved and he no longer needed steroids. Five years later, when the incident was reported to me, the boy's asthma was still controlled without the use of steroids.

This case seems to indicate that therapies like chiropractic and osteopathy do work in the treatment of non musculo-skeletal disorders, despite the fact that they employ principles which are not verifiable from a scientific, anatomical or physiological standpoint. The sleepy states which were induced by treatment, hint that physical therapy was not all that the boy received and that some kind of trance-like state may have been involved. Having examined the usual format of chiropractic treatment, it is evident that some form of suggestion and preconditioning can occur and it could have been this, and not the actual manipulation, which perhaps caused the improvement in the boy's health.

Cranial Techniques

Perhaps the trance state element of healing is more obvious in cranial osteopathy, and its chiropractic cousin sacro-occipital technique. These techniques are based on the rather incredible assumption that healing can be imparted to a sufferer by very gently moving or manipulating the plate-like bones of the skull (cranium). It is believed that subluxations of these cranial bones impede the normal circulation of the fluid which bathes the brain and spinal column (cerebrospinal fluid). This, in turn, is said to cause health problems like migraines, visual and hearing disturbances, arthritis, multiple sclerosis and asthma.

It sounds quite plausible until we try to find out what these 'subluxations' are. They are definitely not visible on X-ray as a dislocation of the bones of the skull. Also they

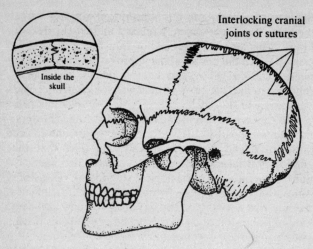

Interlocking cranial joints or sutures

Inside the skull

This drawing shows the interlocking nature of the joints in the bones of the skull. Because of this design it is extremely unlikely that the bones of the skull can move even minutely in any direction. In infants and young children these joints are not fused together so that growth can be permitted, but fusion is complete by the time a person reaches their early teens.

cannot be some problem with the movement of the joints connecting these bones, since they are immovable in anyone over the age of about 15. The immobility of these bones (and their joints) also seems to preclude any movement or manipulation of them. This causes some practitioners to say that their techniques are 'not so much concerned with altering the position of bones as with releasing articular (joint) strains between the structures and restoring physiological motion' (Leon Chaitow). But even a casual glance at the intricately interlocking joints of the bones of the skull (see Illustration above) should be enough to convince someone that cranial bones can't move that much. Furthermore any so-called articular (joint) strains could be relieved just as easily by scalp

Although practitioners of cranial osteopathy and a number of other similar manipulative therapies give reassuring scientific explanations for their treatments, most of what they say is open to question. But when these therapists simply hold their hands above the head, without touching it, the reason for any therapeutic effect is quite definitely not something scientific. Instead it is very likely something psychic or possibly occult.

massage during hair washing as by any specialised gentle touch.

So, I think it is fair to say that this 'hands on' procedure relies more on the actual power of the therapist than it does on any physiological or anatomical mechanism. This seems even more likely when some cranial practitioners claim that they do not need to actually touch the head, but only place their hands slightly above it. The hands held in this way are believed to influence the 'energy waves' over the body. Perhaps this is really a psychic healing technique and it may also be a subtle method of trance induction. Trance induction seems plausible when those who submit to cranial osteopathy report that treatment gives them a warm feeling and makes them relaxed. Some even pass out or fall asleep. Others report being quite unaware that anything is happening, apart from a light touch.

It may also be possible that the cures gained from cranial osteopathy and the other therapies mentioned above are just the result of suggestion or the 'placebo' power induced by the therapy and its practitioner. On the other hand the healing power of these therapies may be the result of some unseen interaction with spiritual forces who are utilising trance states as a way in which they can begin to influence lives, firstly perhaps for apparent good (physical healing), but ultimately for harmful or evil purposes.

Conclusion

During the last hundred years the use of trance states has been confined to the fringes of society. But now, like a kettle coming to the boil, the influence of hypnosis is steaming out from under its previous limitations and is beginning to affect nearly every facet of modern life. Because of its increasing popularity, especially in the field of medicine, Christians are being confronted as never before with the choice of agreeing to be hypnotised or not.

The Main Worries

There are three main worries for those considering hypnotherapy. These are:

1. The loss of control of mind and body that allows someone else's thoughts to be inserted into the subconscious of a hypnotised person. During trance, those who are hypnotised to a level any deeper than light trance will probably not be able to reject or resist these thoughts as they are suggested. Also afterwards they will usually not remember if these thoughts and influences were their own or the hypnotist's. This loss of personal control has been known to lead to physical as well as mental abuse.

2. Trance states as experienced during hypnotherapy may expose the hypnotised person to occult oppression or intrusion. For Christians, who have been

spiritually affected during trance, this may begin with their faith in Jesus being undermined. As a result they may lose confidence in God and his involvement with them in dealing with their difficulties and failings. Instead they may start to use self-orientated methods of life improvement. This may then lead on to them abandoning their Christian beliefs for Hindu/Buddhist ideas such as reincarnation.

Other severe consequences of demonic oppression or intrusion may develop as a result of trance induction. For example, uncontrollable habits, deviant behaviour, panic attacks, brief episodes of loss of consciousness, depression and other forms of emotional disorder. Perhaps, more seriously, trance induction may lead to demonic possession. This may cause clairvoyant/mediumist experiences and multiple personality phenomena. Possession can also lead to severe mental illness possibly culminating in the sufferer taking his own life.

3. Hypnotherapy may well mask or change the symptoms of a disease without dealing with the root cause. This may lead to the misdiagnosis of an illness, or it might mean that the real problem is discovered too late for proper treatment to be effective.

What the Bible Says

Several men in the Bible talked of having experiences which may be referred to as 'trance states'. Isaiah, in chapter 6 of his book and Ezekiel in chapters 1, 8, and 40–48 of his writings, recorded having undergone states compatible with trances. In the New Testament, Peter experienced something similar at the house of Simon the tanner (Acts chapter 10), as did Paul when he was in the temple in Jerusalem (Acts 22:17). Perhaps more arresting is the experience of John in his Revelation. In this, the last book of the Bible, John relates how he was *in the spirit on the Lord's day* (1:10) and how in chapter 4 and verse 1 *the spirit came upon him'* in order to show him visions about the future.

From these passages in the Bible we learn that God has created a kind of 'doorway' in man which allows him to have deep spiritual experiences without the constraints of normal human consciousness. It appears that this doorway is designed for God's exclusive use and so when men and women open themselves up to altered states of mind through hypnosis, they may also be exposing themselves to spiritual forces that are not of God.

Case histories from both the past and the present seem to confirm this suspicion. Those who have submitted themselves to hypnosis, especially deep trance states, have often either displayed paranormal abilities or have had some strange experience of a spiritual, and probably occult, nature.

What is Hypnosis?

In hypnosis, as in all trance states, we are dealing with the interface between man's neurological gift of consciousness and his God given privilege to have spiritual relationship and experience. This ability to relate spiritually was designed to be solely with God the Trinity, but, with man's fall, he has become vulnerable to the influence of other and rebellious spirit beings. Trance states initiated by human beings through ritual, suggestion and passivity in the subject only expose people (very often unknowingly) to the oppression of these ungodly spiritual forces.

The Bible teaches that spiritual relationship with God is possible when a person opens the 'front door' of their life to Jesus (see Revelation 3:17). Following the metaphor, maybe hypnosis and all humanly induced trance states can be regarded as the 'back door' to the deep part of the personality which is known as the spirit. When this back entrance is opened, experience has shown that the human spirit can be exposed to spiritual forces whose motives will not be as laudable as the hypnotist's perhaps are.

When physical healing takes place during hypnosis, it may be due to some placebo response. However it is more likely to be the result of interference by evil spirit forces who are utilising the spiritual vulnerability caused by hypnosis. The healings themselves are usually only transitory and often lead those who have benefited by them into worse suffering and oppression.

Appendix

Quotes from Books on Hypnotism

These quotes are all taken from books written by either practising hypnotherapists or research psychologists. In each case the book being quoted from is fully described in the bibliography, and a key number (e.g. B.1) indicates which one is being used, followed by the appropriate page number. I have attempted to use all the quotes strictly within the context in which they were written. In some cases I have felt that some explanation of the words in a quote is required; in these cases all explanations are placed in brackets with the initials *ADB* at the end of the explanation.

Quote A.

'In order to hypnotise a willing and co-operative subject (the only kind who can be hypnotised under most circumstances) the hypnotist uses a number of methods to lead the person to relinquish some control to the hypnotist and to accept some reality distortion.'

(NB: This quote was taken from a book by E.R. Hilgard, perhaps one of the foremost authorities on hypnosis.) (B.5 page 178)

Quote B.

'Amnesia of Events during Hypnosis – this is usually complete in somnambulism, but the events may be recalled during subsequent hypnosis or the subject may be told to remember them in the course of the normal waking state. With very deep hypnotic states, however (the 'hypnotic coma' of Braid), it may be impossible to recover any memories of what has passed during trance.'   (B.9 page 28)

Quote C.

'The hypnotic trance – the medium through which the therapist works – is accurately measurable in duration and depth.'   (B.1 page 12)

Quote D.

'The purpose of the hypnotic state, from the hypnotist's point of view, is to increase the suggestibility of the subject. This always occurs when true hypnosis is induced and the reason for it is that in an hypnotic state the critical faculties are completely or partially suspended.'   (B.1 page 24)

Quote E.

'Responsiveness to suggestion is only part of hypnosis. When subjects are encouraged to go deeper into hypnosis, they eventually reach a state in which they are unresponsive to the hypnotist's suggestions (except when a pre-arranged signal returns them to a level at which they can communicate). In describing this state, subjects often use terms similar to those used to describe mystical experiences, such as separation of mind from body, a feeling of oneness with the universe, a sense of gaining knowledge, but of a kind that is not communicable' (Tart, 1972).

(B.5 page 179)

Quote F.

'Mesmerism, shorn of many of the trappings of the "baquet" (large oak tube containing a mixture of water, powdered glass and iron filings, *ADB*) the soft music and the showmanship came to be used by a few

British doctors (Elliotson, Esdaile, *ADB*) not only as a general therapy, but for the very practical purpose of removing pain in surgical operations.'

(B.34 page 39)

Quote G.

'As the essence of successful hypnotic induction lies, to a great extent, in the ability of the operator to manipulate the imagination of the subject, it may be useful to make a point of finding out beforehand something about the profession or occupation of the subject.' (B.9 page 44)

Quote H.

'Patients have sometimes been successfully hypnotised in this manner* without their knowledge or consent when a failure might have been anticipated from a more direct approach.'

(*Hypnotising someone when another person seems to be the subject of attention. *ADB*) (B.9 page 48)

Quote I.

'Hypnotic trance – how does this happen? It happens because, when a person is in a hypnotic trance, his or her conscious mind – which is the seat of the critical faculties – is at rest, for the skill of the hypnotist lies in distracting the conscious mind of his subject so that he may deal directly with the suggestible subconscious.'

(B.1 page 25)

Quote J.

'I practised hypnotic treatment for many years, at first by prohibiting suggestion and later on in combination with Breuer's method of questioning the patient. I can therefore speak of the results of hypnotic or suggestive therapy on the basis of wide experience. If ... any ideal therapy should be rapid, reliable and not disagreeable to the patient, Bernheim's method

fulfilled at least two of these requirements. It could be carried through much quicker – or, rather, infinitely quicker – than analytical treatment and it caused the patient neither trouble nor unpleasantness. For the doctor it became, in the long run, monotonous; in each case, in the same way, with the same ceremonial forbidding the most variegated symptoms to exist, without being able to learn anything of their sense and meaning. It was hackwork and not scientific activity and it recalled magic incantations and hocus-pocus.'
(B.22 page 502)

Quote K.

'The following changes are characteristic of the subject's condition in hypnosis:
1. The subject ceases to make plans. When deeply hypnotised, the subject does not like to initiate activity and would rather wait for the hypnotist to suggest what to do.
2. Attention is re-distributed. Under hypnosis, attention becomes more selective than usual. If the subject is told to listen only to the hypnotist's voice, the subject will ignore any other voices in the room.'
(B.5 page 178)

Quote L.

'Schultz tried to obtain the benefits of age-old practices of oriental Yoga and meditation (especially of Vedic origin) while interpreting their phenomena in the light of Western science.'
(B.33 page 24)

Quote M.

'In this advanced treatment induction of the desired state is brought about by the ocular fixation method whereby the trainee gazes at an object a few feet from his eyes. There is similarity between the hypnoidal state (achieved by Autogenic Training, ADB) and dream sleep (the somnambulistic state. ADB) ... The student here may undergo strange experiences of a religious or mystical character ... and be able ... to experience a total loss of the sense of his individuality and to feel one with the universe, an experience described by practitioners of some oriental types of meditation.' (B.33 pages 21–22)

Bibliography

This is not a complete list of the references used to research this book, but it is a brief guide to help the reader follow up what has been written.

Chapter 2

1. *The Healing Power of Hypnotism* by Shreeve (Thorsons).

2. *Hypnosis – Research, Developments & Perspectives* by E. Fromm & R. Shor (Paul Elek (Scientific Books) Ltd.) 1973.

3. *Open to Suggestion* by R. Temple (The Aquarian Press) 1989.

4. *A Clinical Hypnosis Primer* by G.J. Pratt, D.P. Wood & B.M. Alman (John Wiley & Sons) 1988.

5. *Introduction to Psychology* by E.R. Hilgard, R.L. Atkinson & R.C. Atkinson (Harcourt-Brace Jovanovich Inc.) 7th Edition 1979.

6. *Hartland*s Medical and Dental Hypnosis edited by D. Waxman (Balliere Tindall) 3rd Edition 1989.

7. *Trances* by S. Wavell, A. Batt & N. Epton (George Allen & Unwin Ltd.) 1966.

8. *Dictionary of Hypnosis* by R.B. Winn (Vision Press Ltd.) 1965.

9. *Handbook of Medical Hypnosis* by Ambrose & Newbold (Balliere Tindall) 4th Edition 1980.

10. *Hypnosis* by D. Waxman (George Allen & Unwin Ltd.) 1981.

11. *The Relaxation and Stress Reduction Workbook* by M. Davis *et al*, 2nd Edition 1982.

Chapter 3

12. *Journal of the American Medical Association (JAMA)* February 1960, p. 686. (An article entitled *Hypnosis* by H. Rosen MD.)

13. *Lancet* (1959) Vol. No. 2, pages 480–482.

14. *Archives of General Psychiatry* Vol. No. 28, pages 439–440.

Chapter 4

15. *The Devil's Alphabet* by Dr K. Koch (Evangelization Publishers).

16. *ABC of Occult* by Dr K. Koch.

17. *Hypnosis – Are There any Side Effects?* by M.R. Taylor (Diasozo Trust) 1984.

18. *The Holy Spirit and You* by D. & R. Bennett (Coverdale) 1971.

19. *Something for Nothing* by Sid Roth (Kingsway) 1982.

Chapter 5

20. *Death of a Guru* by R.R. Maharaj with D. Hunt (Hodder & Stoughton) 1977.

21. *Theological Wordbook of the Old Testament* by R. Laird Harris, G.L. Archer Jr. & B.K. Waltke (Moody Bible Inst. of Chicago) 1980.

Chapter 6

22. *Introductory Lectures on Psychoanalysis* by S. Freud, edited by J. Strachey & A. Richards (Pelican/ Penguin) 1976.

23. *Natural Medicine* by B. Inglis (Collins) 1979.

24. *The Medicine Men* by J. Lloyd Fraser (Eyre Methuen Ltd.) 1981.

25. *The Witchhunt in Early Modern Europe* by B.P. Levack (Longman) 1987.

26. *The New Encyclopaedia Britannica* (Encyclopaedia Britannica Inc.) 1985.

27. *The Catholic Encyclopaedia* (The Encyclopaedia Press Inc.) 1914.

28. *Three Hundred Years of Psychiatry 1535–1860* by R. Hunter & I. Macalpine (Oxford University Press) 1963.

29. *Charles Dickens and His World* by J.B. Priestley (Thames & Hudson) 1961.

30. *Trance* by Brian Inglis (Grafton Books) 1989.

Chapter 7

31. *Stress and the Art of Biofeedback* by B.B. Brown (Harper & Row) 1977.

32. *The Power of Self-Hypnosis* by J. Hariman (Thorsons) 1981.

33. *Autogenic Training* by K.R. Rosa with an introduction by A.S. Paterson.

Chapter 8

34. *Hypnosis* by H.B. Gibson (Peter Owen) Ltd. 1977.

35. *Acupuncture Investigated* by A.D. Bambridge (Diasozo Trust) 1989.

36. Autobiography by *Andrew Taylor Still*, a reprint of the 1897 edition in 1972 by Arno Press Inc. for *Medicine & Society in America*.

37. *The Lengthening Shadow of A.T. Still* by A.G. Hildreth, published by Mrs A.G. Hildreth & Mrs A.E. Van Vleck in 1942.

38. *The Chiropractic Story* by M. Bach (De Vorss & Co. Inc.) 1968.

39. *The Cranial Bowl* by W.G. Sutherland.

40. *Gray's Anatomy* edited by Williams & Warwick (Churchill Livingstone) 36th Edition, 1980.

41. *Practical Orthopaedic Medicine* by B. Corrigan & G.D. Maitland (Butterworths & Co.) 1983.